S0-BYA-347

PRACTICAL HANDBOOK ON SPECTRAL ANALYSIS

PRACTICAL HANDBOOK ON
SPECTRAL ANALYSIS

by

V. S. BURAKOV

and

A. A. YANKOVSKII

Translated from the Russian by

R. HARDBOTTLE

Translation edited by

S. TOLANSKY, F.R.S.
University of London

A Pergamon Press Book

THE MACMILLAN COMPANY
NEW YORK

95276

544.6
B945

THE MACMILLAN COMPANY
60 Fifth Avenue
New York 11, N.Y.

This book is distributed by
THE MACMILLAN COMPANY
pursuant to a special arrangement with
PERGAMON PRESS LIMITED
Oxford, England

Copyright © 1964
PERGAMON PRESS LTD.

First English edition 1964

Library of Congress Catalog Card Number 63-16858

This is an edited translation of the original Russian *Prakticheskoye rukovodstvo po spektral'nomu analizu*, published in 1960 by Izdatel'stvo Akademii nauk B.S.S.R., Minsk

MADE IN GREAT BRITAIN

CONTENTS

FOREWORD

In 1959 the 21st Congress of the Communist Party of the Soviet Union and the June General Meeting of the Central Committee of the Soviet Union, set new tasks for speeding up technical progress in industry and building construction and for raising the quality of the materials produced.

In raising the quality of production great importance is attached to setting-up comprehensive and continuous controls over production processes, starting with the raw material and ending with the finished goods. It is particularly important to control the chemical composition in production, which governs many technical characteristics of the goods produced.

Emission spectral analysis is an up-to-date method for controlling the chemical composition of various materials, and has found wide use in industry and in various scientific investigations.

In White Russia spectral analysis is widely used in the iron and steel, metal-working, engineering, instrument-manufacture industries, etc., to analyse ferrous and non-ferrous metals and alloys. Spectral analysis methods are used in geological investigations to determine the composition of White Russian minerals, in particular for minute concentrations of elements in the potash salts of the Starobino deposits. Spectral analysis is now being used successfully in medicine to determine the minute concentration content of elements formed in blood and tissues during various illnesses. Such methods are used in biology, agriculture and criminology.

In view of the development and rapid growth of spectral analysis laboratories, the inadequacy of the literature on spectral analysis is keenly felt. Handbooks published earlier are now regarded as collectors' pieces.

The purpose of the present handbook is to give a short account of the main problems in methods for carrying out the spectral analysis of the materials encountered in practice in industrial laboratories.

Unlike previous publications, this book deals both with visual and photographic methods of spectral analysis. The future of photo-electrical methods is indisputable, but their introduction into industrial spectral analysis laboratories requires time and does not exclude the further development and use of visual and spectrographic methods.

The methods presented in this book, are selected on the basis of data given in the literature and from practical experience in this field in works laboratories in the U.S.S.R. and in particular in the White Russian council of national economy.

Naturally, it is impossible to present in one volume the whole of the theoretical and experimental data and the diverse procedures described in the literature. In view of this, in many cases, instead of delving deeply into the physical essentials of the processes being considered, the authors have simply summarized practical data available. For a detailed study of the principles of spectral analysis more fundamental handbooks should be referred to. Of these, the main ones are listed in the literature references, where reference is also made to papers in journals, monographs, etc. giving fuller data on concrete methodological problems.

The authors wish to thank T. M. Zhbanovaya, L. I. Kiselevskii, M. A. Krivosheyevaya, P. A. Naumenkov, G. V. Ovechkin, Ye. N. Paltarak and A. M. Tokarevaya, who kindly commented on the manuscript of the book. The authors will also be glad to receive readers' comments.

INTRODUCTION

Spectral Analysis and Its Possibilities

Spectral analysis is a physical method for determining the chemical composition of matter. It is based on the study of the spectral composition of light emitted, absorbed or reflected by the material being investigated. By the term "spectral analysis" we shall denote atomic emission spectral analysis.

Atomic emission spectral analysis has a number of advantages over other industrial methods of determining the chemical composition of materials.

A distinguishing feature of spectral analysis is its high sensitivity, since it is possible to determine individual chemical elements in amounts totalling millionths of a milligramme. Only a small amount of material is required, so that the end-product can be analysed and then used in service.

By analysing samples on the basis of their emission spectra it is possible to determine simultaneously almost all the chemical elements in various solids, liquids and gases.

Using up-to-date Russian equipment spectral analysis takes several minutes only. Thus it is possible, for instance to determine the composition of a metal during the melting process. By using high-speed electronic computers it is obviously possible to control not only the composition of the metal during the melting process, but also the process itself.

Spectral analysis laboratories do not require expensive or scarce reagents. The photographic methods require ordinary photographic reagents; with the visual and photo-electric methods the need for chemical reagents completely disappears.

Spectral analysis is more accurate than chemical analysis for determining small concentrations of material, and slightly less accurate when evaluating large concentrations.

Much time, material and work can be saved by using spectral analysis in the national economy and in scientific investigations.

At up-to-date establishments up to 90 per cent of all analyses of metals and alloys are carried out by spectral analysis methods. Chemical methods are mainly used for sulphur and carbon analyses.

In the analysis of complex materials by spectral methods the results of the assessment of the individual elements may be distorted by the presence of additional impurities, the so-called "third-body" effect (cf. p. 43), in the species being studied. At present methods are being developed for minimizing or allowing for these effects. The difficulties that restrict the use of spectral analysis methods are provisional and can eventually be overcome.

Production of Spectra

Light is made up of electro-magnetic radiations of definite wavelength. The wavelength of light is measured in angstroms (Å) (1Å = 10^{-8}cm). Red rays have a wavelength of about 6500 Å, green rays of 5300 Å, violet rays of 4100 Å (Table 1). Rays of various wavelengths are present in the radiation from most light sources.

The radiation spectrum of any light source can be produced very simply by means of a triangular transparent glass prism (Fig. 1). On passing through

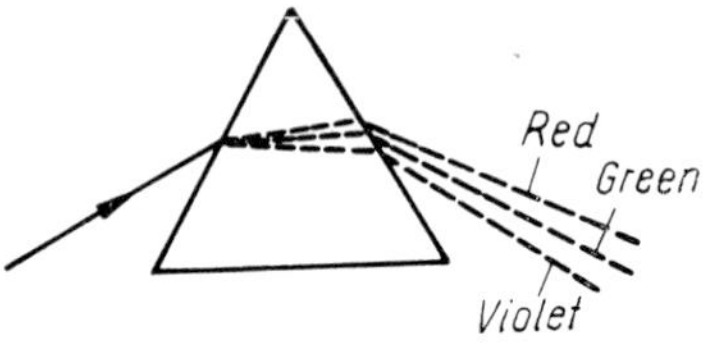

FIG. 1. Splitting of light into a spectrum by means of a prism.

the prism the light forms a band of colour which is the optical spectrum of the source. The action of the prism is based on its different refraction of light to various wavelengths. The red rays, of long wavelength, are only refracted slightly, the green rays are refracted more strongly, and the violet rays (short wavelength) are refracted even more strongly. Thus pencils of colour issue from the prism at different angles and we see light that is split up according to its wavelengths.

The human eye can detect only a narrow spectral colour range. By means of special instruments it can be shown that beyond the red region there is an infrared region and beyond the violet region there is an ultraviolet region. In order to work in this part of the spectrum quartz prisms are used, since glass only transmits visible light together with a very small proportion of the ultraviolet rays. Most spectral analysis instruments contain a glass or a quartz prism.

Light can also split up into a spectrum by other methods. Nowadays increasing use is being made of instruments containing a diffraction grating instead of a prism, i.e. a glass or metal plate on which a large number of parallel equidistant grooves have been ruled by means of a diamond point (the grooves being 1 μ or less apart).

The very narrow apertures of the diffraction grating act each as independent sources when light falls on them, and they radiate the light in all directions.

As a result of diffraction and interference, the light falling on the grating splits up into a spectrum. Several spectra are produced and are arranged symmetrically with respect to the central pencil of light. The further a spectrum is from the central pencil, the "longer" and, as a rule, the less clearly defined it is.

By means of a reflecting diffraction grating it is possible to obtain spectra in the visible, ultraviolet and infrared regions.

In addition to diffraction gratings, our industry now produces high-quality and inexpensive copies of gratings, the use of which greatly lowers the cost of spectral analysis instruments.

The methods used to record spectra differ, and depend on the length of the light wave. In the visible region of the spectrum direct visual observation is possible. In the longer- and shorter-wave regions spectra can be detected by means of the photographic plate, photo-electric cells and other means. Spectral analysis methods are classified as visual, photographic and photo-electric, according to the recording method used.

Spectra and the Structure of Atoms

Emission spectra can be obtained from any self-contained light source. The emission spectra depend on the state of aggregation of the material. The luminous filament of an incandescent lamp, or molten metals emit continuous spectra. In the gaseous state, e.g. in a flame, molecular compounds radiate spectra in the form of more or less broad bands. The spectra of atomic vapours are characterized by the presence of a large number of very narrow lines of differing brightness (line spectra).

The atomic spectrum is one of the most fundamental characteristics of a chemical element. The spectrum of each chemical element of Mendeleyev's Periodic Table, differs from that of all the other elements.

The line character of atomic spectra is connected with structure of the atom. According to present views, each atom consists of a positively-charged nucleus with negatively-charged electrons moving round the nucleus in specified orbits (Fig. 2).

The atomic number of a chemical element in Mendeleyev's Periodic Table agrees in number with the charge of the nucleus of the given atom and with its number of electrons. Each atom has its own set of electron orbits. In the normal state the electrons follow orbits immediately adjacent to the nucleus. When energy is imparted to the atom (by heating the gas to a high temperature or by other means), it undergoes excitation and its electrons move into orbits further removed from the nucleus. The greater the energy, the further from the nucleus are the orbits into which the electrons are removed.

When sufficient energy is imparted to the electron, it may be torn from the atom and leave the zone of attraction of the nucleus. The atom then becomes a positively-charged ion.

To denote neutral atoms the Roman numeral I is written after the symbol of the chemical element (i.e. Fe I, Al I, Cu I, etc.). To denote ionized atoms in which one electron has been removed, the Roman numeral II is written after the symbol of the element (Fe II, Al II, Cu II). To denote a doubly ionized atom the number III is used, etc. (e.g. Fe III, Al III, Cu III; Fe IV, Al IV, Cu IV).

Each electron orbit can be characterized on the basis of the energy required to excite the atom into the corresponding excitation state. Thus, each atom

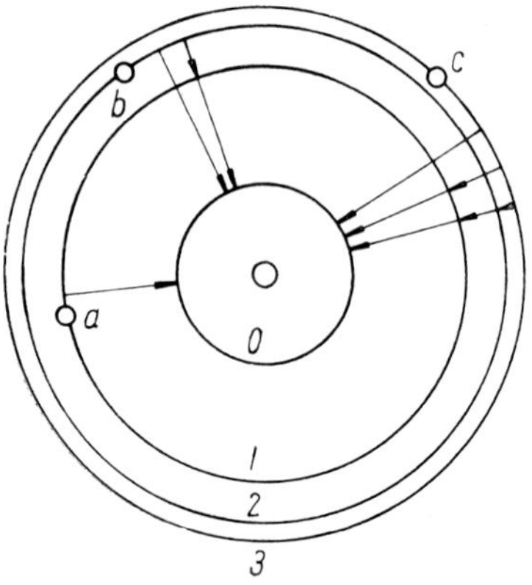

FIG. 2. Diagram showing light emission by an atom.

0—electron orbit of unexcited atom; *1, 2, 3*—electron orbits in excited states *a, b, c;* the arrows indicate the possible transition directions of the electron.

has a definite set of excitation states or set of energy levels. The different excitation states of the atom are characterized by the excitation energy.

Atoms will not remain for long periods in an excited state. They regain the more stable normal state, as a result of the electron jumping to lower orbits. Then a pulse (quantum) of light energy is emitted. The size of the pulse of light energy emitted depends on the positions of the orbits involved in the electron jump. The ionization of an atom also requires a certain energy, the amount differing in the case of different chemical elements.

In atomic spectroscopy the energy is often expressed in electron volts (eV); 1 eV is the energy acquired by an electron in an electric field when it falls through a potential difference of 1 V.*

* In the literature the excitation energy is also expressed in wave numbers (cm^{-1}). If the wavelength is expressed in angstroms, then the energy of a light quantum expressed in wave numbers equals $10^8/\lambda$

The energy E emitted by an atom is inversely proportional to the wavelength of light λ:

$$E = \frac{hc}{\lambda}$$

where h and c are constants. The greater the light energy quantum, the shorter is the wavelength of the light emitted.

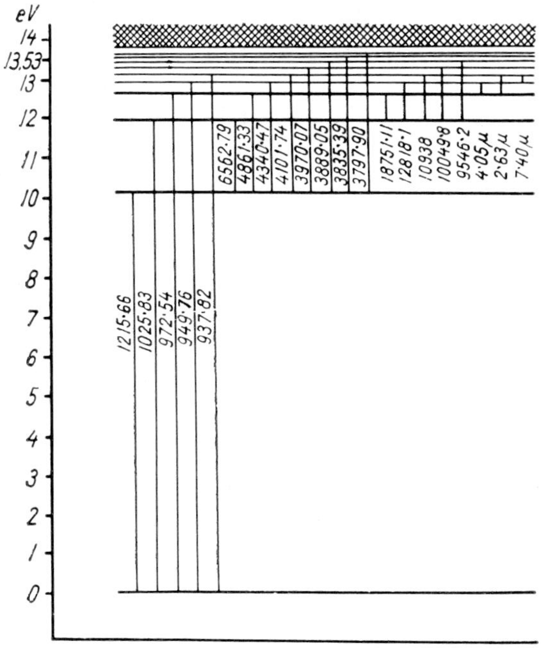

FIG. 3. Energy level diagram of a hydrogen atom.

The set of energy levels of an atom depends on the structure of the atom the charge of the nucleus and the number of electrons. Figure 3 illustrates the energy levels of the simplest atom hydrogen. Here the energy states which the atom can occupy, are depicted as parallel lines corresponding to the energy levels. When the atom passes from a higher energy state to a lower, light of a specific wavelength is radiated. The difference between the energies of the two levels is associated with the wavelength of the light emitted by the atom, by the relation

$$\Delta E = \frac{hc}{\lambda}$$

Expressing the energy in electron volts and the wavelength in angstroms, we get:

$$\Delta E = \frac{12395}{\lambda}$$

From this equation it can be found, for example, that for the spectral line Na I 5896 Å emitted when the electron passes into the stable normal state, the excitation level has an energy of 2·1 eV:

$$\Delta E = \frac{12395}{5896} \approx 2{\cdot}1 \text{eV}$$

The other lines of sodium, emitted when the electron falls from higher upper levels to the normal level, have shorter wavelengths. This follows from the fact that their excitation energies exceed 2·1 eV.

Similarly it is found that the spectral line of hydrogen H I 6568·8 Å, with an upper energy level of 12·09 eV, is emitted when the electron passes into the 10·2 eV level.

Only the outer, valence-electrons participate in the emission of the spectral lines. The number of valence-electrons in an atom differs for different chemical elements. Thus the alkali elements lithium, sodium, potassium, etc. contain only one electron in the outer shell. These elements have simple spectra. Such elements as manganese and iron have five or six valence-electrons, and their spectra are very complex. Chromium, tungsten, molybdenum, tantalum and the rare earths also have complex spectra. Generally speaking, the structure of an atom is closely bound up with its optical spectrum.

Chemical elements can be clearly distinguished from each other on the basis of their spectra. In a material being analysed, the presence in the spectrum of spectral lines of an element, indicates the presence of this element in the sample being studied. The more clearly defined are the spectral lines of this element, the greater is its content in the specimen being analysed.

Thus, spectral analysis involves the determination of the presence in the spectrum of the sample being analysed, of the spectral lines of chemical elements (qualitative spectral analysis) and on the measurement of the intensity of these spectral lines in order to determine the quantities of the elements in the sample being analysed (quantitative spectral analysis).

CHAPTER I

LIGHT SOURCES FOR SPECTRAL ANALYSIS

LIGHT sources for spectral analysis should be capable of exciting atoms, i. e. imparting sufficient energy to them to produce atomic spectra. The light sources may be various flames, electric arc and spark discharges, or gas discharges at low pressure.

The electric light sources—arc and spark discharges—have been most widely used in practice in spectral analysis, the material under investigation being applied to, or forming one of, the electrodes.

The temperatures produced in electrical discharges are sufficient to bring all chemical compounds into the gaseous state, split them up into atoms and excite these atoms.

1. DIRECT CURRENT ARCS

A d.c. arc can easily be produced by a d.c. supply with a d.c. voltage of 120–220 V and an output of 1–2 kW. The electrical diagram of the arc (Fig. 4) includes a rheostat *3* for controlling the current intensity, an ammeter *2* for measuring the d.c., connecting leads and a support holding the electrodes *1*. In order to strike the arc it is necessary to bring the electrodes into contact with each other and gradually draw them apart until there is a gap of several millimeters between them.

When it is necessary to work with a prescribed arc gap, the arc is struck by touching both electrodes simultaneously with a carbon rod. Then the rod is removed and the arc is thus produced. The knife switch *5* serves to cut off the arc.

It should be noted that the supply for the arc may give an insufficiently stable d.c. This is found particularly in the case of low arc currents. In order to secure a satisfactory d.c. supply, a.c. is used in most cases (Fig. 5). After ordinary rectification a pulsating rectified current is obtained, that has constant direction but changes in magnitude 100 times per second (Fig. 5). With pulsating current the current intensity is nil in the intervals between the half-cycles, and the arc may easily be extinguished.

The current pulsations can easily be reduced by means of a stabilizer. In the simplest case the stabilizer may consist of capacitors and a choke designed for an output of 1–2 kW (Fig. 6). Instead of the choke a transformer winding of suitable output can be used. A group of electrolytic capacitors *1* (1000–2000 μF) is connected in parallel with the source of rectified current, whilst a choke

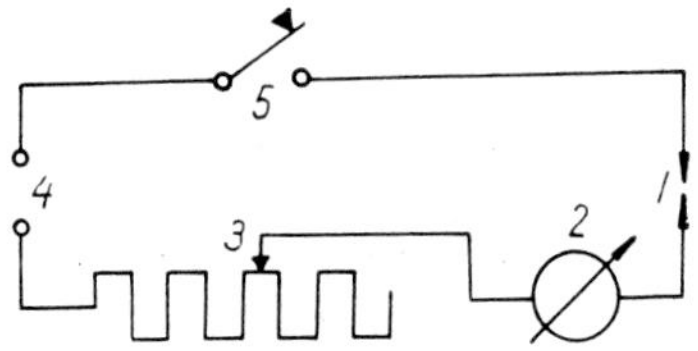

FIG. 4. Electrical diagram of d.c. arc.

1—arc gap; *2*—ammeter; *3*—rheostat; *4*—terminals for connecting d.c. supply source; *5*—switch.

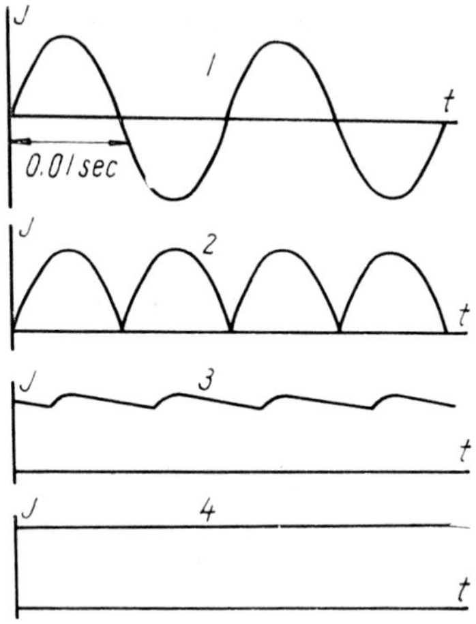

FIG. 5. Current used to feed light sources.

1—a.c.; *2*—pulsating current; *3*—stabilized pulsating current; *4*—d.c.

2 is connected in series, following the capacitors. As a result the variation in the current with time is smoothed. An arc stabilized in this way will strike easily with low currents.

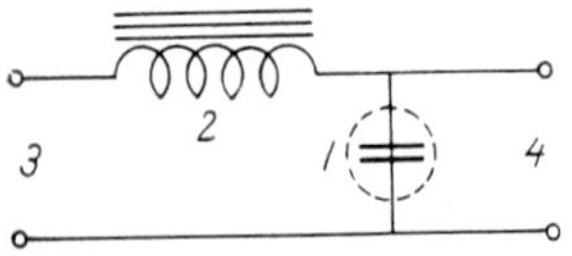

FIG. 6. Diagram of stabilizer for feeding d.c. arc.

1—capacitor; *2*—choke; *3*—terminals for connecting pulsating current; *4*—terminals for feeding arc with stabilized current.

The d.c. arc is one of the best sources for use in qualitative spectral analysis.[(5)] It is highly sensitive for the determination of most chemical elements. Spectral lines of most metals will appear in the arc when the sample contains 10^{-4} to 10^{-6} per cent of the metals.

The d.c. arc can be used for the qualitative and semi-quantitative analysis of various samples that do not conduct current, in particular for the analysis of mineral raw materials in geological investigations. However, this source is not very stable and is hardly ever used for quantitative determinations. Quantitative spectral analysis is usually carried out with an a.c. arc.

2. ALTERNATING CURRENT ARCS

Alternating current arcs are fed from 127–220 V mains and are not usually produced spontaneously. If an arc is struck in some way, it will be extinguished as the polarity of the current changes, which takes place 100 times per second.* Non-continuous arcing can be maintained if the arcing interval is closed 100 times per second. In the circuit of an arc proposed by Sventitskii,(22) the discharge takes place as the result of a preliminary breakdown of the discharge gap ("analysis gap") by means of a low-power high-voltage spark. This circuit is the one on which Russian arc generators are based.

PS-39 Arc Generator

The basic electrical circuit diagram of this generator is shown in Fig. 7. It consists of an arc circuit I and a maintaining device II, fed from a common current source.

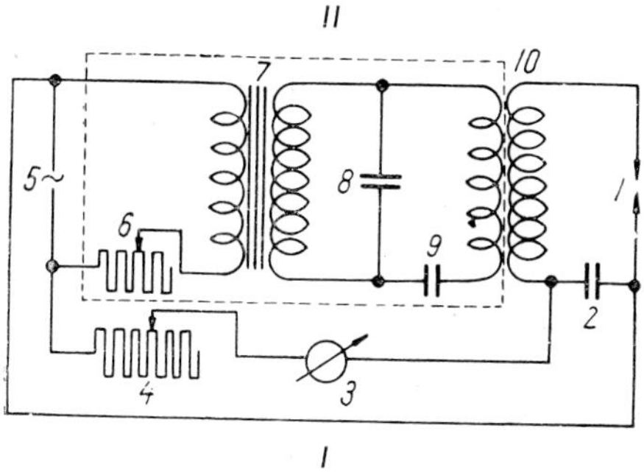

FIG. 7. Electrical system of PS-39 generator.

I—arc circuit; II—maintaining device; 1—arc gap; 2—blocking capacitor; 3—ammeter; 4—arc rheostat; 5—terminals for a.c. mains; 6—transformer rheostat; 7—transformer; 8—discharger; 9—capacitor of high-frequency circuit; 10—air-cored transformer.

We will now consider the operation of the maintaining device. Alternating current at a voltage of 127–220 V reaches the primary winding of the transformer 7 from the mains 5 via a rheostat 6. A high-voltage (about 3000 V) is induced in the secondary winding of the transformer, and during a half-cycle

* At atmospheric pressure a voltage of about 3000 V is required for the electric breakdown of a 1 mm layer of air between metallic plates.

of the a.c. charges the condenser *9* to the voltage necessary to break down the discharge gap *8*. After this breakdown high-frequency electromagnetic oscillations are set up in the electrical circuit comprising the gap *8*, the capacitor *9* and the inductance of the primary winding of the air-cored transformer *10*. The oscillation frequency depends on the capacitance and inductance, and is given by $\nu = 1/2\pi\sqrt{(LC)}$. If the capacitance is in farads and the inductance in henrys, then we get the number of oscillations in cycles per second. In arc generators the frequency is about 500,000 c/s.

By means of the coil of the step-up air-cored transformer *10* the high-frequency oscillations are transmitted to the discharge circuit of the arc, consisting of the capacitor *2*, the inductance of the secondary winding of the transformer *10* and the analysing gap *1*. The voltage of the high-frequency oscillations attains 30–45 kV. However, because of the high frequency and the very low output such a discharge presents no serious danger to the investigator. At the same time this voltage is quite sufficient to ensure breakdown of a gap between electrodes several millimetres apart.

As a result of the breakdown, an arc discharge is produced, that lasts slightly less than one half-cycle of the a.c. As the polarity of the current changes, the arc is extinguished. But now the high-frequency spark again breaks down the arcing gap and again the arc is struck. Thus, a.c. arcs burn in the form of separate flashes, which are struck and extinguished 100 times per second.

The arcing conditions can be changed, chiefly through altering the current intensity by varying the resistance of the rheostat. The arcing also depends on the conditions of the maintaining high-frequency spark. Each individual flash will increase or decrease in length depending on the point in the half-cycle of the a.c. at which the discharge of the maintaining spark takes place.

In order to protect the a.c. mains against the high voltage of the arc circuit, the capacitor *2* is connected in parallel with the analysing gap (Fig. 7). At mains voltages of low frequency (50 c/s.) this capacitor (0·25 μF) offers a considerable resistance. At high frequencies its resistance is only several ohms. At the same time the inlet leads and the turns of the rheostat windings offer a very high resistance at high oscillation frequencies.

Thus the high-frequency electro-magnetic oscillations circulate in the discharge circuit and virtually do not reach the mains.

A general view of the generator is shown in Fig. 8.

It is usually possible to obtain a current of up to 10 A from the PS-39 generator. In order to obtain larger currents a coil of 100 to 200 turns of thick copper wire (2–3 mm) can be connected in parallel with the secondary windings of the aircored transformer, and leads capable of withstanding high current intensities can be led to the terminals of the generator. In this way currents of up to 50 A can be obtained.[23]

In certain cases it is necessary to work with low arc currents (e.g. in the spectral analysis of low-melting metals, wire, foil, small components, and in the

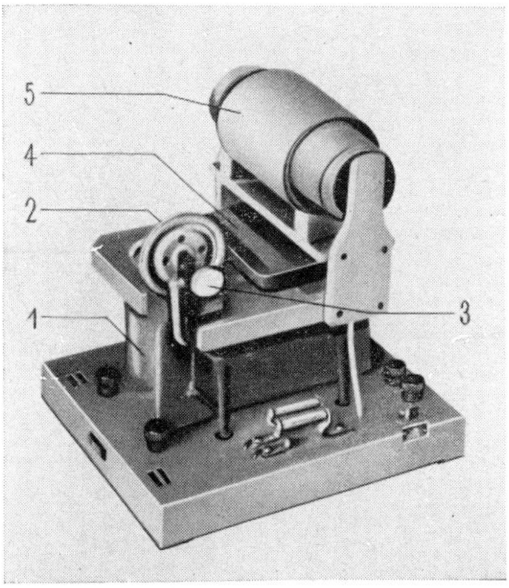

FIG. 8. PS–39 arc generator.

1—transformer; *2*—discharger; *3*—screw for adjusting size of air gap in discharger; *4*—capacitor of high-frequency circuit; *5*—air-cored transformer.

spectral determination of the thickness of metal coatings). But with the ordinary PS-39 generator, on reducing the current to 2–3 A the arc starts to burn very unsteadily, and then the arc gives way to a low-power spark.

The current in the discharge circuit of the PS-39 generator is made up of the mains a.c. and the flashover current of the blocking capacitor. The mains current depends on the resistance of the arc rheostats. A very small current is required to charge the blocking capacitor throughout a half-cycle of the a.c. The discharge of the capacitor takes place very rapidly, in 10^{-4} to 10^{-5} sec, and is oscillatory. In the course of each discharge of the capacitor the current alters direction several times and rapidly falls in magnitude. The maximum value of the current during the discharge may reach several amperes.

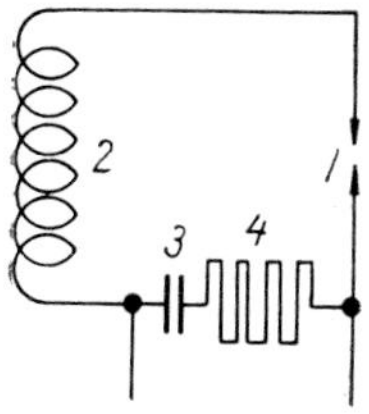

FIG. 9. Production of low currents of an a.c. arc.

1—arc gap; *2*—inductance coil (secondary winding of air-cored transformer; *3*—blocking capacitor; *4*—resistor.

If the mains current is smaller than the amplitude of the current of the oscillatory discharge of the capacitor, then the total current may fall to nil and the arc discharge will cease. In order to ensure steady arcing at low currents, the oscillatory discharge of the blocking capacitor has to be converted into a single-polarity discharge or into an aperiodic discharge.

In the latest versions of the PS-39 generator for this purpose a 2-μF capacitor and a 40–50 Ω resistor are connected in parallel with the blocking capacitor.[24] But an easier way is possible. Steady arcing at currents of less than 1 A can be achieved by connecting a resistor *4* (40–50 Ω) in series with the blocking capacitor *3* (Fig. 9). This procedure also improves the steadiness of the arc at higher current densities.

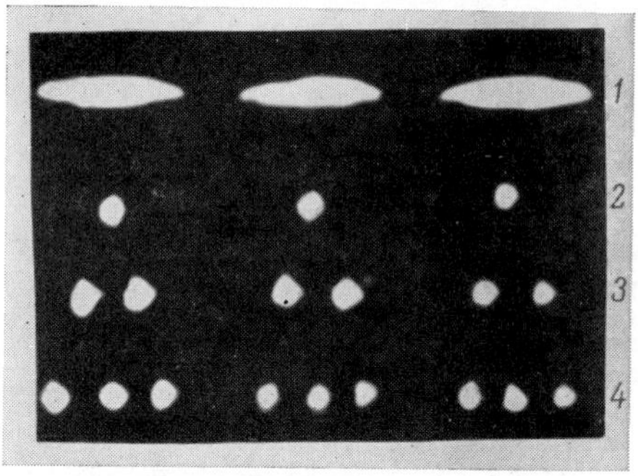

FIG. 10. Determination of the number of unit electrical discharges per half-cycle of the a.c., by means of a vibrating mirror.

1—a.c. arc; *2, 3, 4*—spark with one, two and three unit discharges per half-cycle of the a.c.

Before starting work with the PS-39 generator the leads should be attached correctly, the ammeter and the rheostats should be connected and the gap setting should be checked. The leads from the "arc" terminal must be connected to the stand holding the electrodes, and the gap should be set at 2–3 mm. Then the high-frequency spark should be adjusted to ensure breakdown of the analysing gap. This is done by disconnecting the leads from the "arc rheostat" terminals, setting the cursor of the transformer rheostat at about centre, plugging-in the generator to the mains and pressing the cut-out button. A weak oscillation should flash between the electrodes: otherwise the size of the discharge gap should be reduced. After a spark has been produced, it should be adjusted until a steady humming discharge noise is obtained with no crackling or discontinuity. This is done by adjusting the resistance of the transformer rheostat and the size of the gap. Usually a steady discharge can be obtained by raising the resistance to a maximum and reducing the gap to a minimum. The gap should be adjusted with the generator switched off. If the resistance is low a large current will pass through the primary windings of the transformer, and the transformer will severely overheat and may burn out. If the gap is raised above 1·5 mm, then the capacitor of the high-frequency circuit will become charged at a high voltage, which may cause a breakdown.

The steadiness of the high-frequency spark can be checked visually by means of a mirror or a flat sheet of glass. By vibrating the mirror it is possible to see the image of the spark. When the total amplitude of the mirror vibrations is sufficiently large, time scanning of the arcing can be achieved. We will study a group of oscillations separated by dark spaces (Fig. 10). Each group of oscillations corresponds to one half-cycle of the a.c., i.e. to a time of 0.01 sec. The high-frequency spark should be adjusted to produce a uniform number of single scintillating discharges, or preferably, one discharge every half-cycle of the current.

After the high-frequency arc has been steadied, the arc rheostats are connected to the generator and the required current intensity selected. Each standard PS-39 generator is provided with a data sheet giving instructions for erecting and installing the generator, and also for locating and remedying faults. When a generator or any other spectral analysis equipment is delivered, the equipment and their condition should be checked immediately, and where necessary the manufacturers should be made to repair or replace damaged equipment. The manufacturers guarantee the equipment for one year after it commences operation.

The DG-2 Generator

This is a more efficient generator than the PS-39 generator.* With it the conditions of excitation of the spectrum can be controlled within wider limits.

Figure 11 shows the basic electrical diagram of this generator. With this generator provision is made for producing low arc currents. A resistor *11* is incorporated in the circuit of the secondary winding of the transformer, in order to improve the steadiness of the high-frequency spark.

The high-frequency spark can be used as an independent light source. In this case an inductance coil *15* together with a capacitor *14* for raising the power of the discharge, are incorporated in the circuit of the high-voltage spark. This light source only damages test pieces very slightly, and is suitable for the analysis of small components, that can be used in service when the spectral analysis has been completed.

---

*The DG-2 generator is a modified and improved version of the DG-1 generator. Radio interference in the electrical circuit is prevented by filters and efficient screeining of the current-carryng leads. The industrial production of DG-1 and PS-39 generators has been discontinued.

With the DG-2 generator it is also possible to obtain a low-voltage spark. For this, an additional capacitor *17* (12μF) is connected in parallel with the capacitor *2*, that is charged by volts from the mains. As soon as breakdown of the analysing gap *1*, takes place, the capacitor *17* rapidly discharges.

The nature of the low-voltage spark depends on the mains voltage and on the capacitance and inductance of the discharge circuit. The DG-2 generator can operate at two values of the inductance of the discharge circuit, since an additional capacitor can be connected in parallel with the main capacitor.

The low-voltage spark discharge conditions largely depend on the state of the high-frequency maintaining spark. The number of low-voltage spark discharges per half-cycle of the a.c. is determined by the number of high-voltage spark discharges.

With respect to its spectrum, the low-voltage spark differs appreciably from an arc. In the arc spectrum, arc spectral lines are mainly found, these

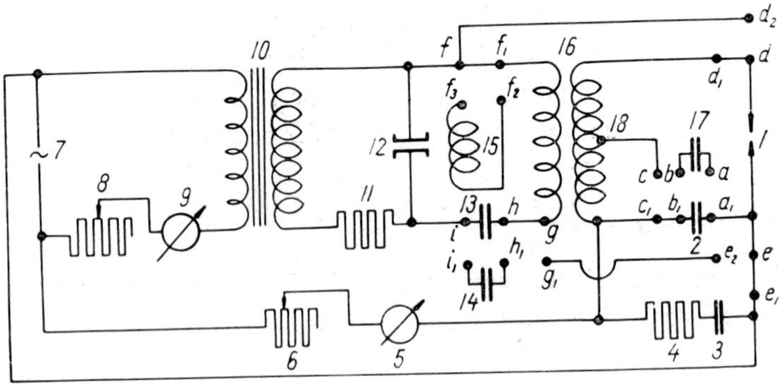

FIG. 11. Basic electrical diagram of DG-2 arc generator.

1—arc gap; *2*—blocking capacitor; *3*—capacitor and *4*—resistors for producing low arc currents; *5*—arc ammeter; *6*—arc rheostat; *7*—terminals for a.c. mains; *8*—transformer rheostat; *9*—transformer ammeter; *10*—transformer; *11*—resistor for stabilizing maintaining spark; *12*—discharger; *13*—capacitor of high-frequency circuit; *14*—extra capacitor for high-frequency spark regime; *15*—extra inductance for high-frequency spark regime; *16*—air cored transformer; *17*—extra capacitor for low-voltage spark regime; *18*—link for low-voltage spark regime with a low discharge-circuit inductance. The contacts a-a_1, b-b_1 and c-c_1 are closed in the low-voltage spark regime; in the high-frequency spark regime the contacts d-d_1, e-e_1 and f-f_1 are opened and the contacts d-d_2, e-e_2, f_1-f_2, f-f_3, g-g_1, h-h_1 and i-i_1 are closed.

belonging to the neutral atom. The low-voltage spark spectrum is characterized by the excitation of a large number of spark lines characteristic of the ion. The high-voltage spark spectrum also contains a large number of lines of ionized atoms.

Thus, with the DG-2 generator greater variation of the conditions of excitation of the spectrum is possible, than with the PS-39 generator, and it is possible to select the optimum conditions for carrying out spectral analysis. A general view of the generator is shown in Fig. 12.

The generator must be earthed. When the generator is connected to the mains a neon lamp on the top panel lights up. On pressing the starter button on the front panel of the generator, or the button on a remote switching

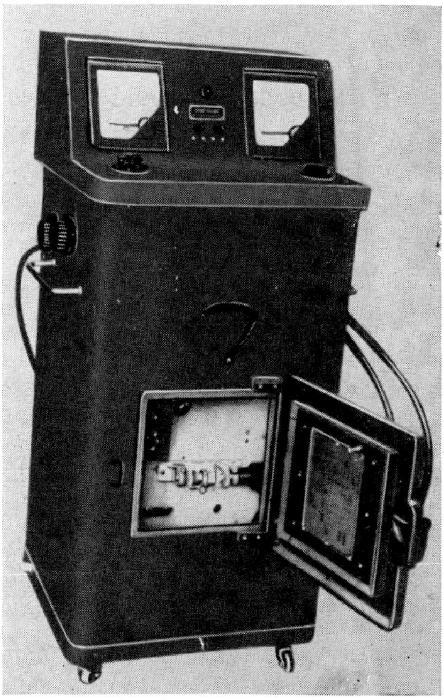

FIG. 12. External view of DG-2 arc generator.

equipment, an electrical discharge should take place between the electrodes held in the stand. If no discharge takes place, the value of the current in the primary winding of the transformer should be increased, by turning the drum located on the left-hand side of the generator, until a discharge takes place across the gap. If the discharge is unsteady, it can be steadied by adjusting the size of the auxiliary gap by means of the button located at the bottom of the right-hand side of the generator. Then the current intensity is set at the required level and work can begin.

In order to obtain high currents (up to 20 A), the current intensity of the arc should be lowered to the minimum before the generator is connected, otherwise the fuses may burn out.

DG-2 generators often have to be used in the absence of an assembly rack. In such cases, when the generator is connected to other racks, the end sockets for the three-pin plug of the rack on the right-hand wall of the generator should be closed by a conductor.

Difficulties may be experienced with this generator due to troubles with the magnetic starter. In this case loud jarring noises may be heard in the generator, the arc or spark discharge may be intermittent, or it may stop completely. The generator should then be switched off and its top cover removed. First, it should be seen whether the struts bracing the cores of the electromagnet are in their sockets. Then the generator should be connected to the mains and the closing of the starter contacts should be checked several times, by actuating the starter button. Sometimes the magnetic starter fails to operate when the starter button is pressed, because the gap between the cores of the electromagnet is excessively large. In this case a piece of insulating material (wood, textolite, etc.) should be packed beneath the armature of the electromagnet at the bottom of the magnetic starter. The thickness of the packing should be such that the magnetic starter closes the contacts satisfactorily; however, the electromagnet should not remain in the closed state after the "stop" button has been operated.

3. SPARK GENERATORS

High-voltage spark generators are often used in the quantitative analysis of metal samples. The electrical circuits of such generators are simpler than those of arc generators.

The main item of a spark generator is a high-voltage transformer *4* which raises the mains voltage to 12000 V (Fig. 13). A capacitor *2* (0·01–0·02 μF)

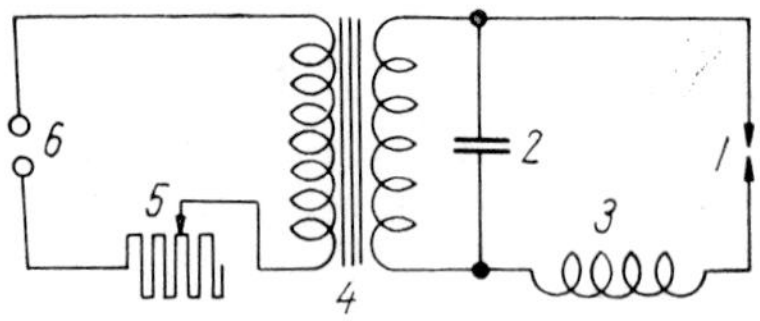

FIG. 13. Electrical diagram of high-frequency (non-adjustable) spark generator. *1*—spark gap; *2*—capacitor; *3*—inductance; *4*—transformer; *5*—rheostat; *6*—terminals for a.c. mains.

is connected in parallel with the secondary winding of the transformer. In the course of a half-cycle of a.c. the capacitor is charged to the voltage required to break down the 3–4 mm discharge gap *1*. The discharge of the capacitor takes place in a time interval that is many times shorter than the charging time. In view of the high speed of the discharge, its power attains values hundreds of times greater than the mean power of the current supplied to the generator.

By varying the current, the length of the gap, and also the capacitance and the inductance, it is possible substantially to alter the spark discharge conditions, which govern the excitation of the spectrum in the spark. As the capacitance rises, for example, there is an increase in the energy of the individual spark discharges and in the brightness of the spectrum. The intensity of the spectrum also increases with the current strength. The intensity of the spark spectral lines falls with increase in the inductance.

IG-3 Generator

In the high-voltage spark diagram described above, the breakdown voltage of the discharge gap depends on a number of factors, viz. the size of the discharge gap, the material, shape and treatment of the electrodes. These drawbacks are overcome in the adjustable high-voltage spark diagram developed by Raiskii.(25)

The basic electrical circuit of the adjustable spark (Fig. 14) differs from that described above in that it contains an auxiliary gap *5*. In addition a large resistor *2* is connected in parallel with the analysing gap *1*. When the capacitor *3* is charged to the required voltage, breakdown of the auxiliary gap *5* takes place. The length of this gap remains constant, and thus breakdown takes place at a virtually constant difference in the potentials of the capacitors. After this breakdown most of the fall in voltage goes to the resistor *2* and the analysing gap *1*, the length of which is slightly less than that of the discharge

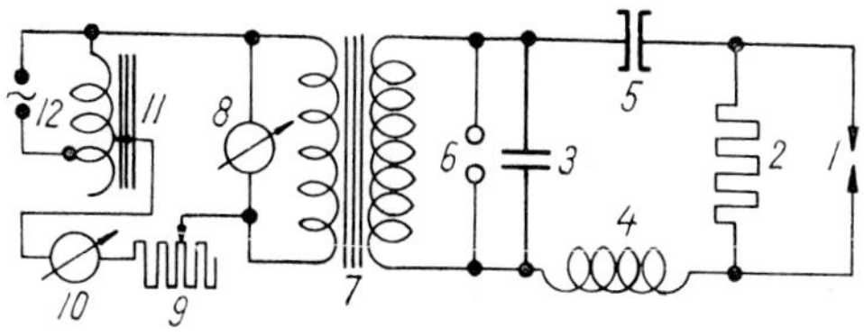

FIG. 14. Basic electrical diagram of IG-3 generator.
1—spark gap; *2*—branch resistor; *3*—capacitor; *4*—inductance; *5*—discharger; *6*—protective gap; *7*—transformer; *8*—voltmeter; *9*—transformer rheostat; *10*—ammeter; *11*—auto transformer; *12*—terminals for a.c. mains.

gap *5*. The oscillatory high-frequency electrical discharge passes through the gap separating the electrodes more easily than through the resistor.

In the circuit being considered, the breakdown of the analysing gap takes place virtually irrespectively of its size and state.

The IG-3 spark generator illustrated in Fig. 15 is based on this electrical circuit.*

FIG. 15. IG-3 spark generator.

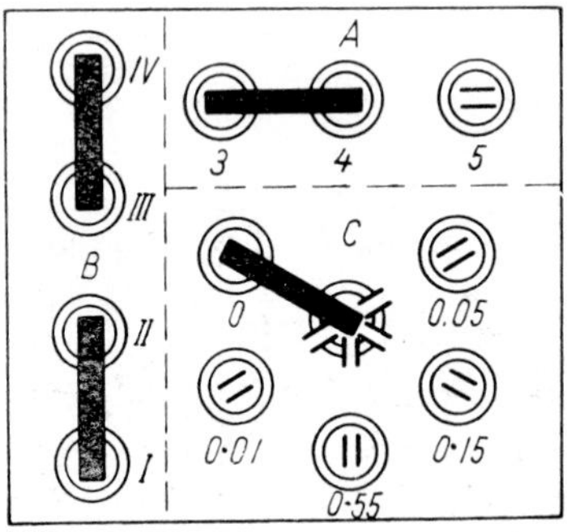

FIG. 16. Panel for varying regimes of IG-3 generator.

A—terminals for varying regimes; *3-4*—complex connexion; *4-5*—simple connexion. *B*—terminals for varying capacitance; *I-II*—0·01 μF; *II-III*—0·005 μF; *I-II, III-IV*—0·02 μF. *C*—terminals for varying inductance (inductance in mH given by figures next to terminals).

* The electrical system of the IG-3 generator is the same as that of the IG-2 generator made earlier. Like the DG-2 generator, it causes neither interference in the mains nor radio interference.

Because of the wide limits within which it is possible to vary the electrical parameters of this spark generator, the conditions of excitation of the spectrum can also be varied within wide limits. Figure 16 illustrates such variations in the discharge regime. The operations of connecting the required capacitance and inductance, and also those of achieving simple and complex connection of the generator (non-adjustable and adjustable spark) are carried out by closing the corresponding pairs of terminals by means of knife switches. The discharge parameters should be varied only when the generator is disconnected from the mains.

Before the generator is connected to the mains, the earthing and the setting of the protective gap spheres should be checked (the distance between the spheres should be 5·5 mm). If the distance exceeds that mentioned, then breakdown may occur in the high-voltage capacitors or in the leads of the secondary winding of the transformer. When the protective gap is too small, the spark discharge will pass between the spheres and there will be no discharge across the analysing gap.

After the generator has been switched on it is set at the required current and voltage (usually 220 V). When currents exceeding 2 A are to be produced, the current intensity in the primary winding of the spark transformer should be lowered before the current switch is put in the position "above 2 A".

4. ARC ATTACHMENT FOR USE WITH HIGH-VOLTAGE SPARK GENERATOR

By using an arc attachment it is also possible to obtain a.c. arc, and low- and high-voltage spark regimes with an IG-3 generator.[26]

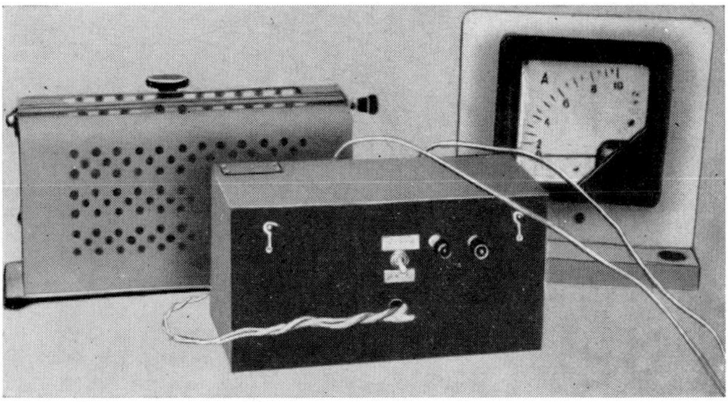

FIG. 17. Spark attachment with rheostat and ammeter.

A general view of the attachment is shown in Fig. 17, while its electrical circuit is shown in Fig. 18.

The main item in the attachment is an air-cored transformer *7* with two single-layer windings. The primary winding of the transformer consists of 20 turns of PEL copper wire 1·5–2 mm in diameter, diameter of turns 80 mm. The secondary winding consists of 80 turns of PEL copper wire 0·6–0·8 mm in diameter, diameter of turns 60 mm. In order to work with high currents two secondary windings can be used, or the diameter of the wire of the secondary winding can be increased to 1·5–2 mm. Reliable insulation consisting of several layers of electrical board and varnished cloth impregnated with bakelite lacquer, should be provided between the primary and the secondary windings.

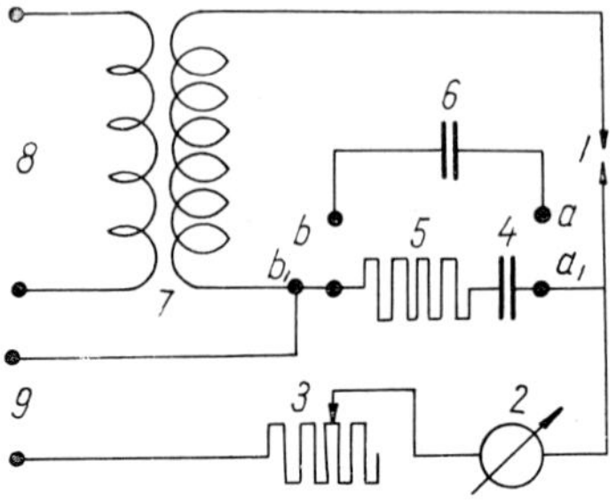

FIG. 18. Electrical diagram of spark attachment.

1—analysing gap; *2*—ammeter; *3*—rheostat; *4*—blocking capacitor; *5*—resistor; *6*—capacitor for low-voltage spark regime; *7*—air-cored transformer; *8*—terminals for connecting high-voltage spark generator; *9*—terminals for a.c. mains. In order to connect the spark attachment to the low-voltage spark regime the contacts aa_1 and bb_1 are closed.

When operating with an arc attachment, an IG-3 or IG-2 generator is connected according to the complex diagram and serves as an activator, breaking down the analysing gap.

In order to obtain an a.c. arc the IG-3 generator is connected as follows: capacitance 0·005 μF, inductance 0, current in primary winding of transformer and voltage minimum. The high-voltage leads of the first generator are connected to the primary winding of the air-cored transformer. The leads from the main are connected to the rheostat and the ammeter, in parallel with the blocking capacitor *4*. In order to produce a steady arc at low currents, a resistor *5* (10–40 Ω) is connected in series with the capacitor *4*. The low-voltage spark is produced by using the same circuit diagram as that used to produce the arc, except that a capacitor *6* (10-40 μF) is connected in parallel with the blocking capacitor *4*.

To produce a high-frequency spark the low-voltage arc circuit is disconnected. By altering the parameters of the high-voltage spark it is possible to obtain various high-frequency regimes. The stability of the electrical regimes attainable with the arc attachment is comparable with that obtainable in the arc and the spark regimes with the DG-2 generator. The attachment can be made at any works.

5. SELECTION OF THE LIGHT SOURCE FOR SPECTRAL ANALYSIS

The selection of the light source for spectral analysis depends on the following factors: whether excitation of the spectral lines of the elements being evaluated is possible in the light source, whether the analysis can be carried out with sufficient speed and accuracy, and the influence of various effects on the results of the analysis.

Whether or not spectral analysis can be carried out with a given light source, depends on the nature of the sample and of the element being analysed.

In spectral analysis laboratories the specimens may be solids, liquids or gases. Solid specimens which conduct electricity can be analysed in a spark or in an arc. Samples which do not conduct electricity, should preferably be analysed in an arc. A spark is used to determine the composition of small samples and samples of low-melting metals. Liquids can be analysed by arc and spark sources. Gases are usually analysed in spark sources.

The spectral lines of metals can be clearly distinguished in an arc or a spark. The spectra of halides, sulphur, carbon and other poorly-excitable elements are produced most easily in a spark.[28]

The choice of the light source also depends on the region of the spectrum being examined. Thus, the determination of phosphorus and silicon in the visible region of the spectrum, is best carried out in a spark. In the ultraviolet region of the spectrum the lines of phosphorus and silicon are produced most easily in an arc.

The concentration sensitivity, i.e. the extent to which similar concentrations of elements can be distinguished, depends on the type and nature of the light source. When the concentrations of the elements in the samples are low, differences in concentration can best be seen in an arc. In the case of high concentrations the sensitivity is greater when a spark is used.

Through the correct choice of a light source it is possible to reduce the preliminary heating and the exposure times of the sample, and also the analysis time. In fact, when an arc is used, in general no preliminary heating is carried out, and the exposure time is only a fraction of that using a spark.

The results of spectral analysis often depend on the structure of the sample, the form of the chemical compound, the presence of other impurities in the sample, etc. The effect of these factors can be greatly reduced through suitable selection of the type and nature of the light source.

The accuracy of the analysis depends on the reproducibility of the electrical conditions of the discharge. Thus the provision of stable light sources is one of the most important tasks of spectral analysis. At present our industry is producing highly stable generators in which the electrical discharges are controlled by means of radio-engineering methods.

CHAPTER II

VISUAL METHODS OF SPECTRAL ANALYSIS

In visual methods of spectral analysis the spectral lines are radiated into the eye of the observer. Various types of spectroscopes and spectrometers are used to produce and observe the spectra. Because of the simplicity of visual methods, a laboratory worker can learn the procedures for carrying out analyses in 1–2 months.

The wide use of visual analysis in the field of the control and study of the chemical composition of various types of samples, is also due to its speed and economy. With a spectroscope it is possible in 2–4 min to determine the content of six to eight elements in a sample and to estimate the purity of a metal, the grade of an alloy or the nature of a mineral.

The quantitative analysis of a sample with respect to three to four elements by means of a spectrometer takes 7–10 min, but is very accurate. Spectroscopes are used to grade metals and alloys at metal stores, in the foundry, forging and mechanical repair shops of engineering, metalworking and other factories, and in the laboratories of scientific research establishments. Spectroscopic methods can be used in geological exploration to carry out preliminary studies on ores and minerals. The use of the spectrometer in foundry shops to control melting operation, offers great promise.

In different factories in Minsk up to 1500 samples of metal and finished goods are rejected every day on the basis of spectroscope tests. In order to carry out this number of analyses by chemical methods the size of the laboratory staff would have to be greatly increased, at a cost of several million roubles.

1. The SL-11 and SL-10 Spectroscopes

In this handbook we shall simply describe briefly the most commonly used spectroscopes, namely the SL-11 and the SL-10 fixed spectroscopes. A characteristic of these instruments is that the rays pass through the dispersive prism twice. Optical instruments of this type are called auto collimation instruments. Auto collimation spectroscopes are small in size and will effectively separate lines of closely similar wavelength.

Figure 19 illustrates the optical design of the SL-11 spectroscope. Light from the arc or the spark *1* is transmitted via the lenses *2–4* to the slit *5* located at the focus of the objective *7*. The pencil of light is transmitted by the reflecting prism *6* to the objective *7* and falls on the dispersive prisms *8* and *9*.

The rays are reflected by the silvered surface *ab* and transmitted back through the prisms and the objective; then they are transmitted via the right-angle prism *10* and the mirror *11* to the eye-piece *12*. The photometric wedge *13* is designed to attenuate the different lines of the spectrum.

The optical part of the spectroscope is located in a separate case *2* (Fig. 20) and fixed to a plate *6* which also carries the table *1* holding the samples being analysed. The second, "permanent" electrode is a disc of electrolytic copper. The distance between the electrodes is controlled by moving the disc in the vertical direction by means of the knob *13*. The disc can be rotated around ts centre by the knob *12*.

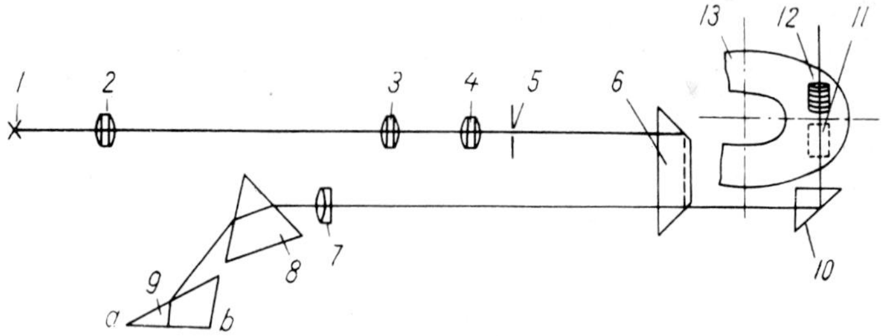

FIG. 19. Optical system of SL-11 spectroscope.

1—light source; *2, 3, 4*—condenser lenses; *5*—spectral slit of spectroscope; *6*—reflecting prism; *7*—objective; *8* and *9*—dispersing prisms; *ab*—silvered surface of prism; *10*—right angle prism; *11*—mirror; *12*—eye-piece of spectroscope; *13*—photometric wedge.

The section of the spectrum required for analysis is brought into the field of view of the eye-piece *4* by rotating the knob *5* that turns the prism. At the same time the objective is refocused, so that the definition of the spectrum remains unchanged.

The photometric wedge is moved by the knob *3*. The divisions on the wedge are read off against a scale that is visible in the field of view of the eye-piece. When it is necessary to work without the wedge it can be removed by means of the knob *3*.

The spectroscope has two interchangeable eye-pieces with magnifications of 12·5 and 20, respectively. The eye-piece with the larger magnification is used to analyse samples that give multi-line spectra (steel, nickel and tungsten alloys, etc.).

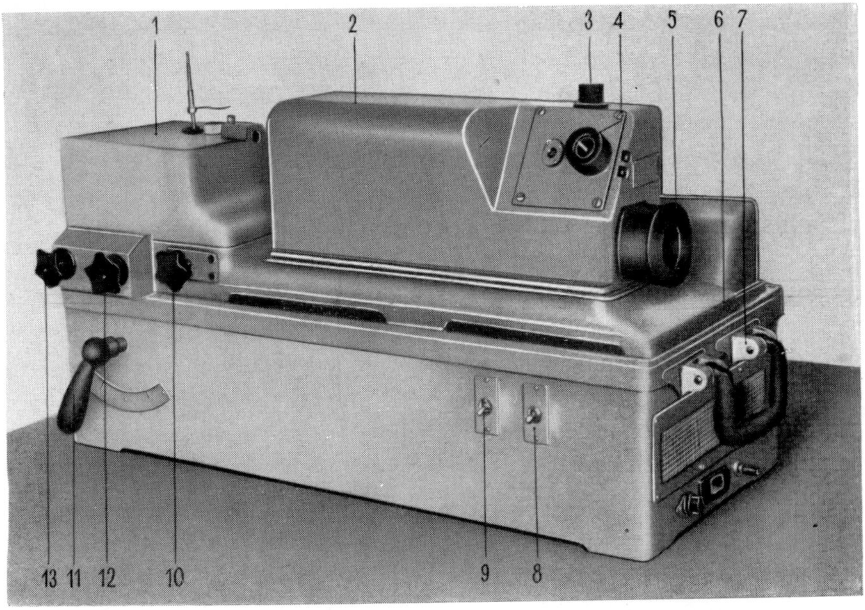

FIG. 20. External view of SL-11 spectroscope.

1—object table; *2*—casing of optical part of spectroscope; *3*—knob for moving photometric wedge; *4*—eyepiece; *5*—knob for rotating dispersing prism; *6*—plate; *7*—casing of arc and spark generator; *8*—current switch; *9*—mains switch; *10*, *12*, *13*—respectively knobs for adjusting permanent electrode relative to optical axis, for rotating the disc electrode and for moving it in the vertical direction; *11*—handle for connecting arc or low-voltage spark regimes.

FIG. 21. External view of SL-10 spectroscope.

1—object table; *2*—disc electrode; *3*—bracket with holder for permanent electrode; *4*—knurled nut for moving bracket carrying permanent electrode; *5*—pin terminals for connecting leads from light source; *6*—condenser; *7*—screen protecting observer from irradiation by ultraviolet light; *8*—eye-piece; *9*—drum for rotating dispersing prism; *10*—test-piece.

In the bottom of the spectroscope there is a generator *7* for producing a.c. arcs and low-voltage sparks. The transition from one regime to the other is effected by operating the handle *11*. By varying the position of the switch *8*, current intensities of 2 or 4 A can be achieved.

The optical design of the SL-10 spectroscope differs slightly from that of the SL-11: instead of the three-lens lighting system a single condenser is used, and there is no photometric wedge.

Figure 21 shows an external view of the SL-11 spectroscope. The sample for analysis is placed on the object table *1*. The permanent electrode, together with the holder *2* and the carrier bracket *3*, is brought to the required distance from the sample by turning the nut *4*. A metal bar can be used as the permanent electrode. It is fixed in a special holder. The leads from a standard arc or spark generator can be connected to the terminals *5*. The light from the source is passed by the condenser *6* to the spectroscope slit, after which its course is the same as that in the SL-11 spectroscope.

2. IDENTIFYING THE SPECTRUM

During arcing between the electrodes a spectrum can be seen in the eyepiece of the spectroscope. It is easy to pick out regions with lines of different colours in the spectrum. Table 1 gives the approximate limits of the wavelengths, expressed in angstroms, for the seven usual colours of the spectrum.

TABLE 1.

Colour	Wavelength interval in Å
Violet	3950–4250
Indigo	4250–4550
Blue	4550–4950
Green	4950–5650
Yellow	5650–5950
Orange	5950–6400
Red	6400–7200

From a knowledge of the wavelengths of each of these regions, it is possible to choose the appropriate part of the spectrum for finding specified lines. The number of lines in the arc or spark spectrum, their position relative to each other and their intensity, will depend on the material of the electrodes. In the spectrum of zinc attention focuses on the three bright lines in the blue region, with wavelengths of 4680·1, 4722·2 and 4810 Å.* In the orange region of the spectrum zinc atoms emit an intense line with a wavelength of 6326·3 Å.

On arcing between copper electrodes, clear green lines of copper (5105·5, 5153·2 and 5218 Å) and several lines the indigo region with wavelengths of 4651·1, 4587·0, 4480·4 Å, etc. will be seen in the spectrum.

It is useful to note the readings on the drum of the dispersive system when the indicator is set to the zinc and copper lines listed above. This will be of help later in studying multi-line spectra, in particular the spectrum of iron.

The spectrum of iron contains a large number of lines, and at first one gets the impression that it is very difficult to identify. However, a more careful study reveals characteristic groups with a given arrangement, brightness and sharpness of the lines. These groups can easily be distinguished in the image of the visible range of the spectrum of iron shown in Fig. 22. An atlas of spectra of this sort is essential for interpreting the spectrum of iron, which is a unique wavelength scale in spectroscopic analysis.

From the atlas we see that in the region of 6400 Å there are two bright lines of iron with wavelengths of 6393·6 and 6400·0 Å. In order to find these in the spectrum we will use the zinc line in the orange region (λ = 6362.3 Å) mentioned above. We find the reading on the drum corresponding to this line. Applying a grain of a zinc salt to one of the electrodes, we check that the range we have taken is the correct one, from the appearance of a bright red line. The iron lines mentioned above will appear a little to the right of this line. We then note the readings of the drum corresponding to one of these lines.

By progressively comparing the atlas and the spectrum being studies, we continue the interpretation proceeding from the longer to the shorter wavelengths. The brightest lines are used as a guide. In the region 6146–6020 Å there are eight intensive lines. In the yellow region of the spectrum it is easy to find the doublet of sodium (Na I 5896 and Na I 5890 Å), which flashes brightly when a grain of table salt is put on one of the electrodes.

The spectrum of iron can easily be identified in the green region because there are several groups each consisting of three to four bright lines (5371–5365 Å, 5434–5424 Å, 5273–5264 Å, etc.).

The part of the spectrum approaching 4200 Å is particularly interesting with respect to visual analysis. In the range 4200–4300 Å about ten very intense iron lines are observable.

In studying the spectrum, at 50–100 Å intervals divisions of the drum will be seen corresponding to the setting of the indicator on the characteristic

---

* Here and later the wavelengths of the lines are given to within an accuracy of 0,1 Å.

lines. In order to obtain the true readings on the drum scale, the drum should be rotated in one direction.

The relation between the drum readings and the wavelength of the lines can be depicted graphically (Fig. 23). This curve, called a dispersion curve, makes it easier initially to find the required part of the spectrum and the individual lines. Each spectroscope has its own dispersion curve. In order to improve the accuracy of the readings based on the dispersion curve, it

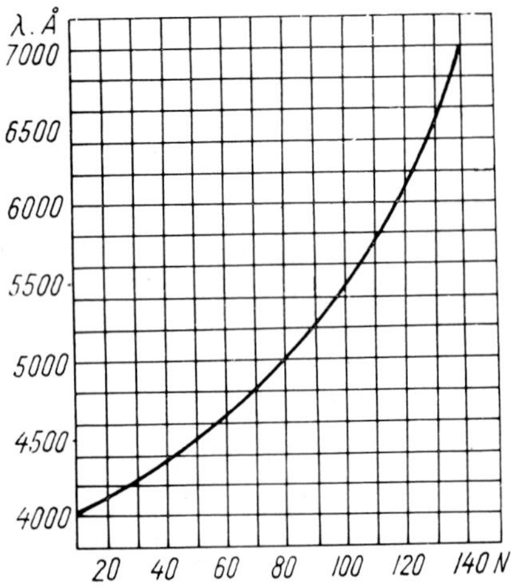

FIG. 23. Dispersion curve of a spectroscope.

should be plotted on millimetre squared paper, with 1 mm equalling 5 Å along the wavelength axis. The divisions of the plate distance should amount to 2 mm.

3. ESSENTIALS OF VISUAL METHODS OF SPECTRAL ANALYSIS

Qualitative Analysis

In the atlas of the iron spectrum (Fig. 22) several manganese and chromium lines are given. The appearance of these lines in the spectra is due to the presence of impurities in the U7 carbon steel used for the electrodes.

Each chemical element has a particular set of spectral lines of given wavelengths. The wavelengths of the spectral lines are given in special tables.[14] The general procedure in qualitative spectral analysis is to determine the wavelengths of the lines observed and to identify them with the data given in the tables.

The wavelength of a line can be determined roughly on the basis of the dispersion curve of the spectroscope. To do this, the line in question is brought up to the indicator and the readings are taken from the drum. After repeating the measurements three to four times the corresponding wavelength is found from the dispersion curve on the basis of the mean value obtained in the measurements. Even when great care is taken in making the measurements, the error in determining the wavelength in this way usually amounts to several angstroms. This sometimes makes it difficult to compare the experimental and the tabulated data; and it is then also difficult to identify the element which the line in question belongs.

The wavelength can be measured more accurately using the visual interpolation method. We will now discuss this method. Figure 24 compares the same parts of the spectra of cast iron I and iron II. The spectrum of the cast iron contains two extra lines. Line *2* more or less divides in half the space between the lines of iron *1* and *4* ($\lambda = 6301\cdot5$ and $\lambda = 6393\cdot6$ Å respectively), the difference in the wavelengths being 92·1 Å. Thus the wavelength of line *2* is

I

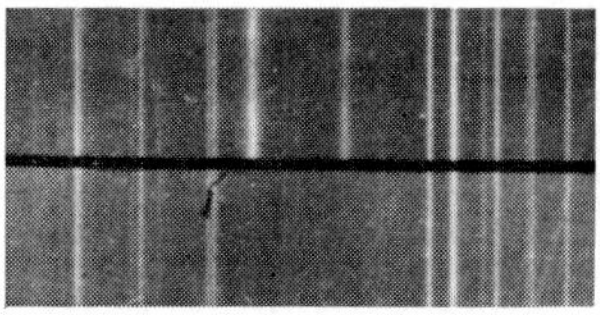

II

FIG. 24. Part of the spectra of (I) cast iron and (II) iron in the red region.

6347·5 Å. The spectral line tables show that in this range there is the silicon II line 6347·0 Å. The other elements contained in the cast iron (chromium, nickel, manganese, copper) do not emit a line of this wavelength.

Knowing lines *2* and *4*, in a similar way we get the wavelength 6370·3 Å for line *3*, which is close to the line Si II 6371·1 Å, given in the spectral line tables. The discovery of a second silicon line confirms our original conclusion concerning the line with a wavelength of 6347·5 Å measured earlier. Now it is possible to state with greater certainty that the analysis sample contains silicon.

In the above example the lines are some distance from each other, and also in the red region, where the dispersion of the instrument is low (cf. Chapter III, Section 1). However, even with an approximate evaluation of the wavelengths we were able to show that the lines belonged to a certain element. In the indigo and violet regions of the spectrum, on selecting iron lines in the vicinity of the unknown line, the error can be reduced many times,

Often it is impossible to find iron lines in the spectrum that are equidistant from the unknown line. In such cases the interval between the iron lines may be taken in the ratio 1:2, 1:4, 2:3, etc.

Figure 25 shows part of the spectrum of steel. Lines *3* and *4* are absent from the spectrum of iron (cf. atlas of iron spectrum). We will determine their wavelengths, knowing the iron lines *1* ($\lambda = 5339{\cdot}9$ Å) and *5* ($\lambda = 5364{\cdot}9$ Å) (difference 25·0 Å). The distance between lines *1* and *3* is about a quarter of the distance between lines *1* and *5*, i.e. 25·0/4 Å $\approx$ 6·2 Å. Adding this to the wavelength of line *1* we get the wavelength of line *3*: $\lambda_3 = 5346{\cdot}1$ Å.

Line *4* obviously divides the distance between lines *1* and *5* in the ratio 1:2. Thus, adding to $\lambda = 5339{\cdot}9$ Å one third of the distance between *1* and *5* we get $\lambda_4 = 5348$ Å. Comparing the values obtained with those in the tables, we easily see that the lines being studied belong to chromium. The tabulated values of their wavelengths are 5345·8 and 5348·3 Å.

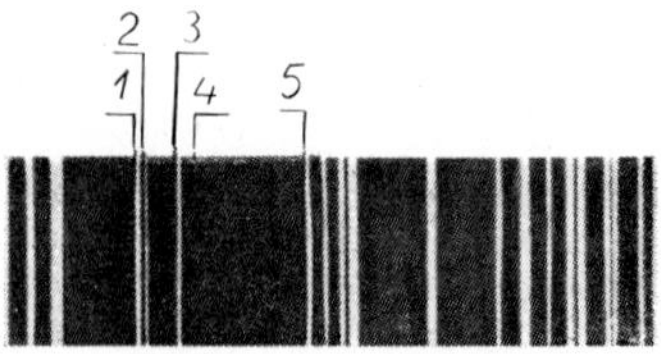

FIG. 25. Part of the spectrum of steel in the green region.

For greater certainty in attributing a line to one or other element, it is useful to refer to the spectra of samples of simple composition containing the element in question. Pure metals, salts of chemical elements, binary alloys, etc., can be used as samples.

In studying powders and solutions, and alloys based on copper, nickel, aluminium, etc., the spectrum of iron can be used as the wavelength scale. Thus it is desirable to use a permanent iron electrode or to resort to the method known as the method of fixing the position of the line of the unknown element. In the latter case the line found in the spectrum of the sample is brought up up to the indicator and, without moving the drum, an arc is struck between the iron electrodes. The position of the indicator, and hence the wavelength of the unknown line, are then determined by the visual interpolation method as described in the examples given above.

Visual qualtative analysis can be used to detect the presence of most chemical elements in various samples: metals, alloys, ores, minerals, etc. The findings thus obtained are often in themselves of intrinsic interest. In addition, in selecting quantitative methods of chemical or spectral analysis it is important to have a qualitative knowledge of the composition of material to begin with. This is practicable by means of a spectroscope.

In carrying out qualitative analyses it is necessary above all to find in the spectrum the standard lines of the elements concerned in the analysis. Such lines are given for the commonest elements in Table 2. In addition to the wavelength of the line, a rough indication is given of its intensity in the arc

TABLE 2. STANDARD LINES OF THE COMMONEST ELEMENTS

Name of element	Wavelength of lines, in Å	Intensity		Wavelengths of interfering lines, in Å
		in arc	in spark	
1	2	3	4	5
Aluminium Al	3961·5	3000	2000	
	3944·0	2000	1000	
	3092·7	1000 R	1000 R	
	3082·2	800 R	800 R	
Antimony Sb	2877·9	250	150	
	2598·1	200	100	Fe 2598·4
	2528·5	300 R	200	Si 2528·5
Arsenic As	2349·8	250 R	18	
	2288·1	250 R	5	Cd 2288·0
Barium Ba	5535·6	1000 R	200 R	Mo 5533·0
	4554·0	1000 R	250 R	
	3071·6	100 R	50 R	
	2335·3	60 R	100 R	
Beryllium Be	2650·8	25	—	
	2348·6	2000 R	50	
Bismuth Bi	4722·6	1000	100	Zn 4722·2 Ti 4722·6
	3067·7	3000 R	2000	Sn 3067·8, Fe 3067·2
	2898·0	500 R	500 R	Mn 2898·0; Nb 2897·8
Boron B	2497·7	500	400	
	2496·8	300	300	
Cadmium Cd	6438·5	2000	1000	
	4799·9	300	300	
	3261·1	300	300	Fe 3261·3
	2288·0	1500 R	300 R	As 2288·1
Caesium Cs	4593·2	1000 R	50	V 4594·1; Fe 4592·7
	4555·4	2000 R	100	Ti 4555·5; Fe 4556·1 Ba 4554·0
Calcium Ca	4226·7	500 R	50 R	
	3968·5	500 R	500 R	
	3933·7	600 R	600 R	
	3179·3	100	400	
	3158·9	100	300	

(TABLE 2 CONTINUED, 1)

1	2	3	4	5
Carbon	4267·3	–	500	
C	4267·0	–	350	
	2478·6	400	400	Fe 2478·6
	2296·9	–	200	Ni 2297·1
Cerium	4137·6	25	12	
Ce	3221·2	50	8	
	3063·0	40	10	Cu 3063·4
Chromium	5208·4	500R	100	
Cr	5206·0	500 R	200	
	4274·8	4000R	800 R	
	4254·4	5000R	1000 R	
	3593·5	500R	400 R	
	3014·8	300 R	100	
Cobalt	4813·5	1000	6	
Co	4121·3	1000 R	25	Fe 4121·8
	3453·5	3000 R	200	Ni 3452·9; Cr 3453·3; Cr 3453·7
	3449·2	500 R	125	
	2286·2	40	300	
Copper	5218·2	700	–	
Cu	5153·2	600	–	
	5105·5	500	–	
	3274·0	3000 R	1500 R	
	3247·5	5000 R	2000 R	
	2961·2	350	300	
	2136·0	25	500	
Gallium	4172·1	2000 R	1000 R	Fe 4172·1
Ga	4033·0	1000 R	500 R	Mn 4033·1
	2943·6	10	20 R	Ni 2943·9; Fe 2943·6
Germanium	4226·6	200	50	Ca 4226·7
Ge	3039·1	1000	1000	Fe 3039·3; In 3039·4
	2691·2	25	15	
	2651·2	40	20	Fe 2651·7
Gold	6278·2	700	20	
Au	5837·4	400	10	
	2676·0	250 R	100	W 2675·9; Co 2676·0
	2428·0	400 R	100	Pt 2428·0; Cr 2428·1

(TABLE 2, CONTINUED, 2)

1	2	3	4	5
Hafnium Hf	4093·2	25	20	Co 4092·4
	2820·2	40	100	
	2641·4	40	125	Th 2641·5
Indium In	4511·3	5000 R	4000 R	
	4101·8	2000 R	1000 R	
	3256·1	1500 R	600 R	Mn 3256·1
	3039·4	1000 R	500 R	Ge 3039·1; Fe 3039·3
Iridium Ir	3220·8	100	30	
	2924·8	25	15	
Iron Fe	4404·8	1000	700	
	4383·5	1000	800	
	4307·9	1000 R	800 R	
	3719·9	1000 R	700	
	3020·6	1000 R	600 R	
	2599·4	1000	1000	
Lead Pb	4057·8	2000 R	300 R	
	2833·1	500 R	80 R	
	2802·0	250 R	100	
Lithium Li	6707·8	3000 R	200	
	6103·6	2000 R	300	
	3232·6	1000 R	500	W 3232·7; Sb 3232·5
	2741·3	200	–	
Magnesium Mg	5183·6	500	300	
	5172·7	200	100	
	2852·1	300 R	100 R	Na 2852·8; Fe 2851·8
	2795·5	150	300	Fe 2795·5
Manganese Mn	4823·5	400	80	
	4033·1	400 R	20	
	4030·8	500 R	20	
	2949·2	100	30	
	2933·1	80	15	
	2801·1	600 R	60	Zn 2800·9
Mercury Hg	4358·4	3000	500	
	2536·5	2000 R	1000 R	Co 2536·0

(TABLE 2, CONTINUED, 3)

1	2	4	4	5
Molybdenum	5533·0	200	100	
Mo	3798·2	1000 R	1000 R	
	3170·3	1000 R	25 R	
	2816·2	200	300	Al 2816·2
Nickel	4714·4	1000	8	
Ni	4401·6	1000	30	
	3414·8	1000 R	50	Co 3414·7;
	3050·8	1000 R	–	V 3050·9; Co 3050·9
Niobium	4079·7	500	200	
Nb	4058·9	1000	400	Pb 4057·8
	3094·2	100	1000	Al 3092·7; Cu 3094·0
	2927·8	200	800 R	
Posphorus	2554·9	60	20	
P	2553·3	80	20	Fe 2553·2
	2535·7	100	30	Fe 2535·6
	2534·0	50	20	
Platinum	4442·6	800	25	Fe 4442·3
Pt	4118·7	400	10	Co 4118·8; Fe 4118·5
	3064·7	2000 R	300 R	Ni 3064·6
	2929·8	800 R	200	
	2659·5	2000 R	500 R	
Potassium	7699·0	5000 R	200	
K	7664·9	9000 R	400	
	4047·2	400	200	
	4044·1	800	400	
	3447·7	100 R	75 R	
	3446·7	150 R	100 R	
Rubidium	7800·2	9000 R	–	
Rb	4201·9	2000	500	band ~~ZN~~ CN
Silicon	3905·5	20	15	
Si	2881·6	500	400	
	2516·1	500	500	
Silver	5465·5	1000 R	500 R	
Ag	5209·1	1500 R	1000 R	Cr 5208·4
	3382·9	1000 R	700 R	Sb 3383·1
	3280·7	2000 R	1000 R	Mn 3280·8; Fe 3280·3

(TABLE 2, CONTINUED, 4)

1	2	3	4	5
Sodium	5895·9	5000 R	500 R	
Na	5890·0	9000 R	1000 R	
	3302·3	600 R	300 R	Zn 3302·6
	2852·8	100 R	20	Mg 2852·1
Strontium	4832·1	200	8	
Sr	4607·3	1000 R	50 R	
	3464·5	200	200	band CN
	3380·7	150	200	Ni 3380·6; Fe 3380·1
Tantalum	3311·2	300	70	
Ta	2714·7	200	8	
Thallium	5350·5	5000 R	2000 R	
Tl	3229·8	2000 R	800 R	Fe 3230·2
	2918·3	400 R	200 R	Fe 2918·4
Tin	4524·7	500	50	
Sn	4511·3	200	–	In 4511·3
	3175·0	500	400	Fe 3175·4
	2840·0	300 R	300 R	Cr 2840·0; Mn 2840·0
	2421·7	130 R	200 R	
Titanium	4991·1	200	100	
Ti	4981·7	300	125	
	3372·8	80	400 R	
	3349·0	125	800 R	
	3088·0	70	500 R	Cu 3088·1
Tungsten	4302·1	60	60	
W	4294·6	50	50	Fe 4294·1
	2947·0	20	18	
	2866·1	15	10	
Vanadium	4384·7	125 R	125 R	Cr 4385·0
V	4379·2	200 R	200 R	
	3185·4	500 R	400 R	
	3184·0	500 R	400 R	
	3110·7	70	300 R	
	3102·3	70	300 R	Ni 3101·6

(TABLE 2, CONTINUED, 5)

1	2	3	4	5
Zinc	6362·3	1000	500	
Zn	4810·5	400	300	Bi 4722·6
	4722·2	400	300	Ca 3344·5; Mo 3344·7
	3345·0	800	300	Na 3302·3
	3302·6	800	300	Cu 2138·5; Fe 2138·6
	2138·6	800 R	500	
Zirconium	4772·3	100	–	
Zr	4687·8	125	–	Fe 3437·0
	3438·2	250	200	
	2722·6	50	50	

Note. The symbol R indicates that the line undergoes considerable absorption in the light source.

and the spark, expressed in representative units according to a 100-point scale. The brighter the line of a given element, the higher is the number denoting the intensity. It will be seen from the table that the region where visual recording of the spectrum is possible, contains standard lines of the alkali and alkaline-earth metals, vanadium, tungsten, gallium, indium, manganese, copper, lead, titanium, chromium, zinc. In order to establish the presence in a sample of any of these elements, it is possible to use visual methods of spectral analysis, which are simple to carry out, and do not require complicated apparatus or chemical reagents.*

Qualitative analysis can be used at works to help in the sorting of carbon and alloy steels, bronzes, brasses and other alloys containing different chemical elements. In this case it suffices to confirm the presence of the lines of these elements in the spectrum and occasionally to make a rough estimate of their intensity. Thus, in carbon steels the concentration of chromium does not generally exceed 9·35 per cent, and of the lines of chromium listed in Table 2 only the more intense will be visible in the spectrum. In the spectra of chromium steels, the chromium lines listed will be unusually bright, and in addition a number of other intense lines will be seen (5345·8, 5348·3, 5409·8 Å, etc.).

* If it is necessary to carry out a complete qualitative analysis of a sample, then it is preferable to employ spectrographic analysis methods, by means of which the presence of a large number of elements can be detected in a single spectrogram.

Similarly, bronzes OTs and OTsS can be distinguished by determining whether the spectrum contains the Pb line 5005·4 Å. Ordinary brass can be distinguished from bronze not containing tin, on the basis of the brightness of the zinc lines. In brasses the zinc content is far higher and thus the lines will be more intense.

Semi-quantitative Analysis

The basis of quantitative analysis is the relationship between the intensity of the spectral lines and the concentration of the element in the sample. Thus, in order to determine the concentration of an element in a test-piece it is necessary to measure the intensity of any one of its lines. This cannot be done using visual methods, because the observer cannot make objective judgements. The judgements of different observers will not tally with each other, because the luminance perception of the eyes of the different observers will not be uniform in a given region of the spectrum.

The intensity of a spectral line can be assessed more accurately by comparing it with another line. As a rule lines of the basic element of the sample are taken as the internal standard lines. The need to resort to internal standard lines is also dictated by the fact that the absolute intensity of the spectrum is subject to large variations, owing to differences in the amount of the material entering the discharge region and the conditions of excitation of the atoms. These differences are due to heating of the samples during the analysis, discrepancies between the amounts of material removed during grinding, variations in the mains voltage, etc. But these factors do not greatly affect the relative intensities of the lines.

The known internal standard line and the unknown comparison line are called analysis pairs. In order to attain a steadier ratio between their intensities, the analysis pair should consist of lines having similar excitation energies. Such lines are known as homologous lines, and the method of using them is called the homologous pair method.

The principle of spectroscopic analysis can be explained on the basis of Fig. 26. When steel contains 0·5 per cent of chromium, line *8* equals in intensity the iron line *4*, while line *7* is far weaker than line *5*. We can say provisionally that $8 = 4$ and $7 \ll 5$. When steel contains 1 per cent of chromium, the intensities of lines *7* and *5* are identical (*7*—*5*). At a chromium concentration of 4 per cent line *7* is much brighter than line *6* ($7 \gg 6$) and lines *8* and *6* are similar in intensity to each other : $7 \gg 6$, $8 \leqslant 6$. By carrying out similar determinations on analysis pairs of samples of known composition, it is possible to obtain a series of analytical relations for determining the content, not only of chromium but of other elements.

Thus, the spectroscopic analysis of alloys is based on the principle of comparison of the intensities of an unknown comparison line and a known internal standard line. The accuracy of the analysis depends a great deal on the selection of the line pairs. It is advantageous where possible to select analysis line pairs of approximately equal intensity for various concentrations of the unknown element. These lines can easily be compared, because the eye will easily see when they are of equal intensity. Thus the concentrations of the element will be determined more accurately.

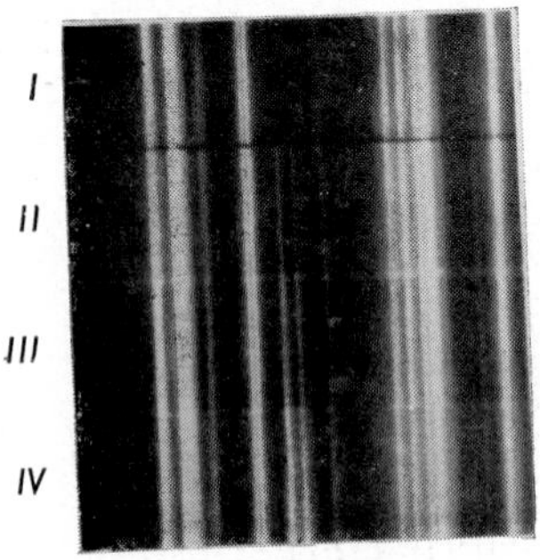

FIG. 26. Relationship between relative intensity of chromium and iron lines, and content of chromium in test-pieces.

I—part of the spectrum of pure iron; II-IV—the same parts of the spectra of steels containing respectively 0·5, 1 and 4–5 per cent of chromium.

If, for instance, the comparison line is far brighter than the internal standard line, it will not be possible to determine the concentration with certainty; the intensities will be in the same ratio to each other when the concentration of the unknown comparison element is much higher. In such cases other analysis pairs should be used. But the choice is limited, especially in the analysis of alloys that give spectra containing small numbers of lines (copper, aluminium and other alloys). This explains the high level of inaccuracy that is permissible in spectroscopic analysis.

In general, the error in determining the concentration of most elements by spectroscopic methods, amounts to one-quarter to one-sixth of the concentration, while in some cases it may be as much as 50 per cent. In order to distinguish spectroscopic analyses from more accurate quantitative determinations, they are usually termed roughly quantitative or semi-quantitative analyses.

In the case of concrete conditions of excitation of the spectrum, the analysis data are given in the description of the procedures for the spectroscopic analysis of alloys. In the cases of other conditions these data should be determined by estimating the ratios of the intensities of the line pairs for samples of known compositions.

4. PREPARATION OF SAMPLES AND ELECTRODES FOR CARRYING OUT THE ANALYSIS

The analysis specimens are cleaned on an emery wheel to remove all scale, paint and surface flaws. The area prepared for analysis should measure about 10×10 mm. To prevent the specimen from being contaminated by the emery material, especially in the case of the determination of silicon, aluminium, and titanium, the area should be finally cleaned by means of a file. A separate file should be used for each type of alloy and metal.

The mass of the specimens should be not less than 50 g. But the possibility of analysing small parts, filings, powder, etc., is not excluded. Before being analysed, filings or powder should be melted, by placing 1–2 g of the sample on the end of a copper electrode. An arc with a current intensity of 5–6 Å is struck between the sample and a second copper electrode. The drop of metal formed is then analysed in accordance with the criteria laid down for solid specimens.[27] The criteria for determining chromium, manganese, silicon, tungsten, molybdenum and vanadium apply during the first 5 min of arcing. But care should always be taken beforehand that the criteria used are suitable for the analysis of small parts.

The material of the permanent electrode should not contain the elements being evaluated in the alloy sample. For the analysis of steels and cast iron a permanent electrode of electrolytic copper containing hundredths of 1 per cent of nickel, silicon and iron is recommended.

The use of iron electrodes is undesirable, owing to the presence in them of manganese, chromium and silicon. In addition, iron electrodes heat up rapidly, forming an oxide coating that blocks the arc gap. A continuous background which is particulary intensive in the red region, will be seen in the spectrum.

The ends of the copper electrode rods 6–10 mm in diameter can be turned on a lathe to form a cone or a truncated cone. But electrodes sharpened to a cone (conical electrodes) soon burn and the analysis gap increases, leading to unsteady arcing, with the result that the reproducibility of the analysis results is impaired. In most cases electrodes sharpened to a truncated cone (wedge-shaped electrodes) or a hemisphere are used. A special cutter with a suitable cutting edge can easily be made for making hemispherical electrodes. The electrodes and the analysis area of the specimen, should be free from cracks, roughness and burr.

In carrying out mass spectroscopic analysis a copper disc 1·5–2 mm thick and 8–10 cm in diameter is used. Such discs are supplied with the spectroscope, and can also be made from electrolytic copper. Disc electrodes can be used withouth cleaning to analyse 25 to 30 samples.

When the specimen is placed on the object table, care should be taken to ensure that its edges do not block the light from the arc.

5. SEMI-QUANTITATIVE ANALYSIS OF STEELS AND CAST IRONS

Chromium, manganese, tungsten, vanadium, nickel and titanium are determined with excitation of the spectrum by an a.c. arc;[4, 20] the arc current is 4–6 A (in the analysis of small parts the current should be lowered to 2–3 A). The permanent electrode is of copper. The length of the analysis gap is usually 2–3 mm.

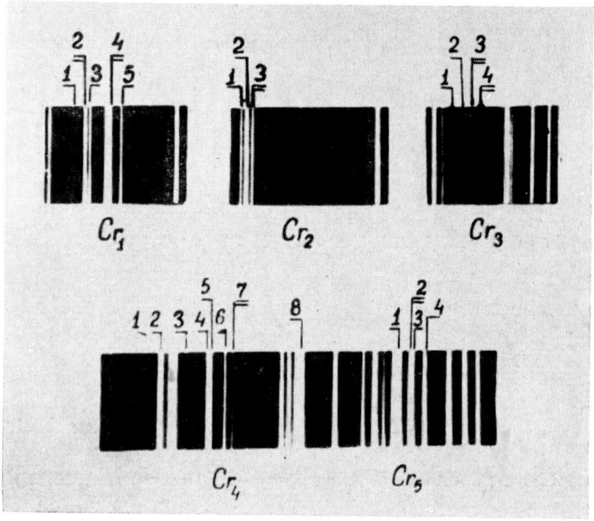

FIG. 27. Line groups for determining chromium.

A high-voltage, or less frequently a low-voltage arc is used to excite the lines of silicon. Lines of phosphorus, carbon and sulphur suitable for analysis purposes can with difficulty be excited under special low- and high-voltage regimes.[28, 29]

The intensity of the lines should be estimated after arcing has continued for 20–40 sec. During this time, called the firing time, there is an uneven supply of material and the ratio between the intensities of the lines of the analysis pairs does not remain constant. During the firing time the required current intensity should be obtained, the spectrum should be focused and the parts of the spectrum containing the analysis lines should be located. Such groups of lines for most elements that are determined in steels, are given in Figs. 27–35. The groups are indicated by the symbols of the corresponding chemical elements.

Contrary to the handbooks,[4, 20] on which the procedures given below are based, in this book the groups of lines for each element are listed in order

TABLE 3. SPECTRAL LINES AND CRITERIA FOR EVALUATING CHROMIUM

Group of lines	Wavelength, in Å	Provisional numeration of lines	Content of Cr, %	Ratio of line intensities in groups				
				Cr_1	Cr_2	Cr_3	Cr_4	Cr_5
	Fe 4643·5	*1*	0·05	*2* not		$3=1$	$6<1$	
	Cr 4646·2	*2*	0·10	$2\leqslant3$, $2\leqslant1$		$3\leqslant1$	$6\geqslant1$	
Cr_1	Fe 4647·4	*3*	0·13	$2=1$, $2<3$		$3=2$	$6>1$	
	Cr 4652·2	*4*	0·15					
	Fe 4654·5	*5*	0·20	$2\leqslant3$, $2\geqslant1$		$3\geqslant2$	$7\geqslant1$	
	Fe 4919·0	*1*	0·3	$2=3$			$6=3$	
Cr_2	Fe 4920·5	*2*	0·4	$2\geqslant3$			$6\geqslant3$	
	Cr 4922·3	*3*						
	Fe 5198·7	*1*	0·7				$7=3$	$2<3$
	Fe 5202·3	*2*	1·0				$6=4$, $7\geqslant3$	$2=3$
Cr_3	Cr 5204·5	*3*	1·5				$6<5$, $6>4$	
	Cr 5206·0	*3*						
	Cr 5208·4	*4*						
	Fe 5321·1	*1*	2·5				$7=4$	$2=4$
	Fe 5324·2	*2*						
	Fe 5333·3	*3*	5				$6\geqslant2$, $7=5$	$2\geqslant1$
Cr_4	Fe 5339·9	*4*						
	Fe 5341·0	*5*	10		$3\leqslant1$		$6=8$, $7=2$	
	Cr 5345·8	*6*						
	Cr 5348·3	*7*	15		$3=1$			
	Fe 5371·5	*8*						
	Fe 5405·8	*1*	20		$3>1$, $3<2$		$6\geqslant8$, $7\leqslant8$	
Cr_5	Cr 5409·8	*2*						
	Fe 5410·9	*3*	30		$3=2$		$6>8$, $7\geqslant8$	
	Fe 5415·2	*4*						

of increasing wavelength, as also are the analysis lines in each group. In this way it is easier to remember the lines and the spectroscopic criteria to be selected for the analysis.

1. Figure 27 gives five groups of spectral lines for evaluating chromium. Table 3 gives the wavelengths of the line pairs and the spectroscopic criteria.

It is suitable to begin the determination with the group Cr_4, which can be used successfully to evaluate concentrations ranging from 0·05 to 30 per cent. Chromium concentrations of 10–30 per cent can be estimated by means of the group Cr_2.

2. Contents of up to 1·5 per cent of manganese can be determined on the basis of the groups Mn_1 and Mn_3 (Fig. 28). If the alloy contains more than

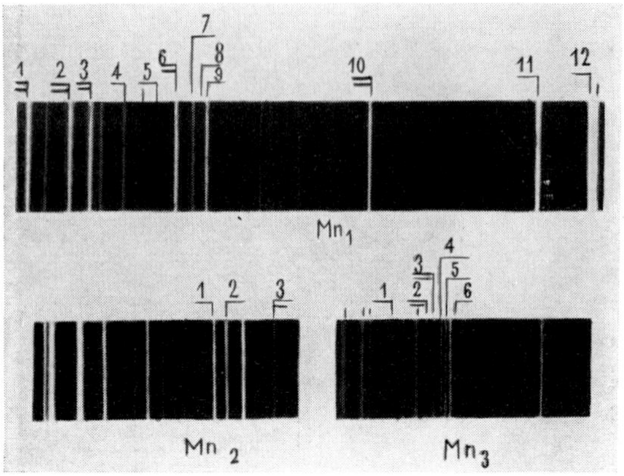

FIG. 28. Line groups for determining manganese.

4–5 per cent of chromium, then it is difficult to detect the lines of group Mn_1. In this case use is made of Mn_3, which has the advantage that the lines in it are located very close to each other and can easily be compressed despite the low sensitivity of the human eye to orange light. At manganese concentrations of 3–14 per cent the lines of group Mn_2 are used. The line wavelengths and the criteria for determining the concentration of manganese, are given in Table. 4.

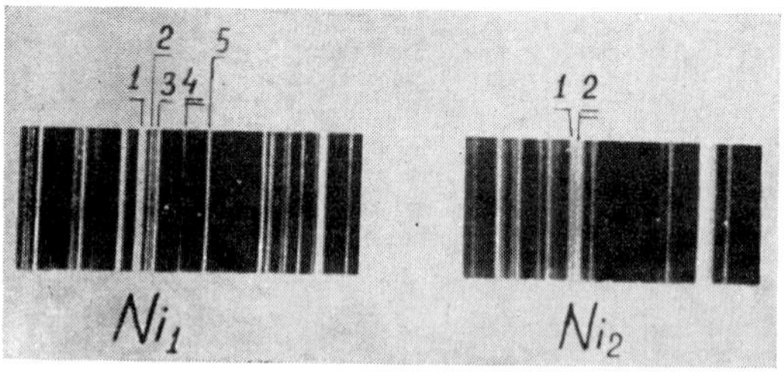

FIG. 29. Line groups for determining nickel.

It should be noted than a spectroscopist can determine contents of 0·5–0·6 per cent of manganese with an absolute error of less than 0·05 per cent.

3. Figure 29 gives two of the line groups characteristic of nickel. Table 5 gives the line wavelengths and the spectroscopic criteria. At nickel contents

TABLE 4. SPECTRAL LINES AND CRITERIA FOR EVALUATING MANGANESE

Group of lines	Wavelength in Å	Provisional numeration of lines	Content of Mn, %	Ratio of line intensities in groups		
				Mn_1	Mn_2	Mn_3
	Mn 4754·0	*1*	0·02	*6<5*		
	Mn 4762·4	*2*				
	Mn 4766·4	*3*	0·04	*6≤5*		
	Fe 4772·8	*4*	0·06	*6=5*		
	Fe 4779·4	*5*	0·08	*6>5; 6=8*		
Mn_1	Mn 4783·4	*6*	0·1	*6<7; 6>8; 6=4*		
	Fe 4786·8	*7*	0·15	*6=7; 6≥4*		
	Fe 4788·8	*8*				
	Fe 4789·6	*9*	0·2	*6≥7; 1<7; 2≤4*		*3≤1*
	Mn 4823·5	*10*	0·25	*6>7; 1=7; 2≥4*		*3≥1*
	Fe 4859·8	*11*	0·3	*1>7; 6≤9; 3≤4*		*3>1; 2≤1*
	Fe 4871·3	*12*				
	Fe 5497·5	*1*	0·35	*6=9; 3≥4*		*2=1*
Mn_2	Fe 5501·5	*2*	0·4	*3≤7; 6≥9; 10<11*		*2≥1; 3<6*
	Mn 5516·8	*3*	0·5	*2≤9; 1=9; 3≥7*		*2>1; 3≤6*
				10≤11		
	Fe 6000·0					
	Mn 6013·5	*1*	0·6	*1>9; 2=9*		*2≤6; 3>6*
	Mn 6016·6	*2*	0·7	*2≥9; 10=11*		*2=6*
Mn_3	Fe 6020·2	*3*	0·9	*10≥11*		*5=4*
	Mn 6021·8	*4*	1·0	*10<12; 10>11*		
	Fe 6027·1	*5*	3		*3≤2*	
		6	7		*3=1*	
			14		*3≥1*	

of 1·5–3 per cent and above, group Ni_2 can be used to check the results. The intensity of the nickel lines in this group undergoes sharp periodic changes in the form of separate sparks, and the ratios between the intensities of the analysis pairs should be determined when the nickel lines are at their brightest.

4. The position of the lines used to determine tungsten, is shown in Fig. 30, while the wavelengths and the intensity ratios of the line pairs are given in Table 6. The group W_2 has the best spectroscopic criteria. It should be used at the start of the determination, and the accuracy of the results obtained therewith should be improved by means of the other groups.

5. Figure 31 shows the groups of lines used to evaluate vanadium. The wavelengths of the analysis pairs and the spectroscopic criteria are given in

TABLE 5. SPECTRAL LINES AND CRITERIA EVALUATING NICKEL

Group of lines	Wavelength in Å	Provisional numeration of lines	Content of Ni, %	Ratio of line intensities in groups	
				Ni_1	Ni_2
Ni_1	Fe 4707·3	*1*	0·03 – 0·05	$4<5$	
	Fe 4709·1	2	0·06 – 0·1	$4\leq5$	
	Fe 4710·3	*3*	0·1 – 0·2	$4=5$	
	Ni 4714·4	*4*	0·25	$4>5; 4<2$	
	Fe 4721·0	*5*	0·5	$4\leq2$	
			1·5	$4=3$	*2* flashes infrequently
Ni_2	Fe 5079·2	*1*	3·0	$4>3; 4<1$	$2<1$ and flashes frequently
	Ni 5080·5	2	5·0	$4=1$	$2\leq1$
			10	$4>1$	$2=1$ and flashes very frequently
			15 – 20		$2>1$, no sparks

Table 7. The most sensitive of the vanadium lines (group V_1) are located in the indigo region of the spectrum. The groups V_2 and V_3 are used in assessing vanadium contents exceeding 0·5-1·5 per cent.

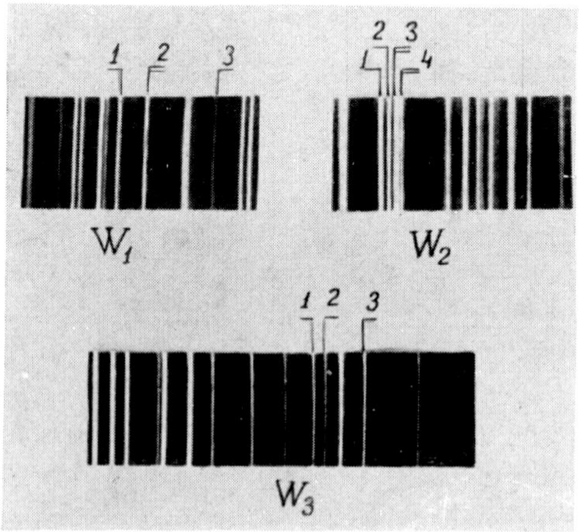

FIG. 30. Line groups for determining tungsten.

6. To evaluate molybdenum the group of lines with the wavelengths given in Table 8 (green region of the spectrum) is most often used. Figure 32 shows

the corresponding part of the spectrum. On the basis of the data given in Table 8, contents of molybdenum as low as 0·1 per cent can be determined.

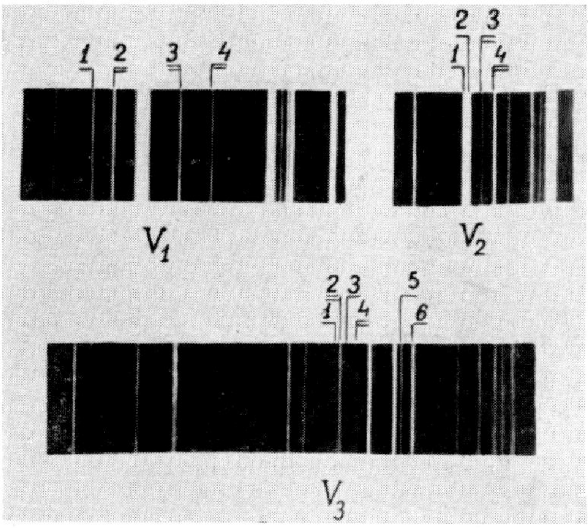

FIG. 31. Line groups for determining vanadium.

7. Table 9 gives the analysis pairs for assessing titanium together with the ratios of their line intensities. The part of the spectrum shown in Fig. 33 includes two titanium lines: 4991·1 and 4999·5. Å. The line Ni 5000·3 Å is superimposed

TABLE 6. SPECTRAL LINES AND CRITERIA FOR EVALUATING TUNGSTEN

Group of lines	Wavelength in Å	Provisional numeration of lines	Content of W, %	Ratio of line intensities in groups		
				W_1	W_2	W_3
	Fe 4654·5	*1*	1·0	*2=3*	*3<2*	
W_1	W 4659·9	2	2·0	*2⩾3*	*3⩽2*	
	Fe 4673·2	*3*	2·5	*2>3; 1⩽1*	*3=2*	
	Fe 5049·8	*1*				
W_2	Fe 5051·6	2				
	W 5053·3	*3*	5·0	*2>1*	*3⩽1*	*3=2*
	W 5054·6	*4*	8		*3⩾1*	*3>2*
	Fe 5497·5	*1*	9		*3⩾1; 4⩽2*	*3⩾1*
W_3	Fe 5501·5	2	13		*3>1; 4=2*	
	W 5514·7	*3*	18		*3≫1; 4⩾2*	*3≫1*

TABLE 7. SPECTRAL LINES AND CRITERIA FOR EVALUATING VANADIUM

Group of lines	Wavelength in Å	Provisional numeration of lines	Content of V, %	Ratio of line intensities in groups		
				V_1	V_2	V_3
V_1	Fe 4375·9	*1*				
	V 4379·2	*2*	0·15	*2=1*		
	V 4390·0	*3*				
	V 4395·2	*4*	0·30	*3=1*		
V_2	Fe 4871·3	*1*				
	Fe 4872·1	*2*	0·50	*4=1*	*3<4*	
	V 4875·5	*3*				
	Fe 4878·2	*4*	0·80		*3=4*	
V_3	Fe 6213·4	*1*				
	V 6216·4	*2*	1·5		*3=2*	*2=5; 4=3*
	Fe 6219·3	*3*				
	V 6224·5	*4*	2·5		*3=1*	*2>5; 4=1*
	Fe 6246·3	*5*				
	Fe 6252·6	*6*				

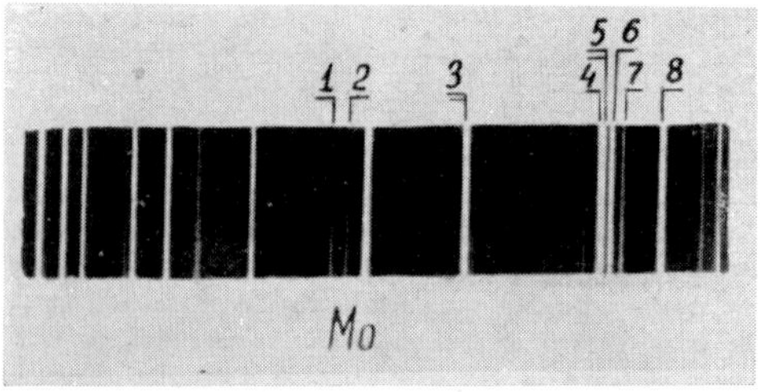

FIG. 32. Line group for determining molybdenum.

TABLE 8. SPECTRAL LINES AND CRITERIA FOR EVALUATING MOLYBDENUM

Wavelength, in Å	Provisional numeration of lines	Content of molybdenum, %	Ratio of line intensities
Fe 5497·5	*1*	up to 0·15	*3≤2*
Fe 5501·5	*2*	0·15-0·30	*3=1; 5≤7*
Mo 5533·0	*3*		
Fe 5569·6	*4*		
Mo 5570·4	*5*	0·35-0·60	*3≤6; 5≤4*
Fe 5572·8	*6*		
Fe 5576·1	*7*	0·65-1·2	*3≤8; 5=6*
Fe 5586·8	*8*	>1·2	*3>8; 5>6*

on the second of these two lines. This superimposition distorts the results obtained on determining low concentrations of titanium (less than 0·1 per cent) when the specimen contains more than 5 per cent of nickel.

TABLE 9. SPECTRAL LINES AND CRITERIA FOR EVALUATING TITANIUM

Wavelength in Å	Provisional numeration of lines	Content of titanium %	Ratio of line intensities
Ti 4991·1	*1*	traces	*3* hardly visible
Fe 4994·1	*2*	0·05	*1*=*2*; *3* clearly visible
Ti 4999·5	*3*	0·1-0·15	*1*>*2*
Fe 5001·9	*4*	0·3	*3*⩽*4*
Fe { 5005·7	*5*	0·35	*3*=*4*
Fe { 5006·1		0·8	*3*=*5*
		1–1·5	*3*⩾*5*

8. In the visible range silicon emits three lines of high intensity: 3905·5, 6347·0 and 6371·1 Å. The first of these lines is located in the marginal violet

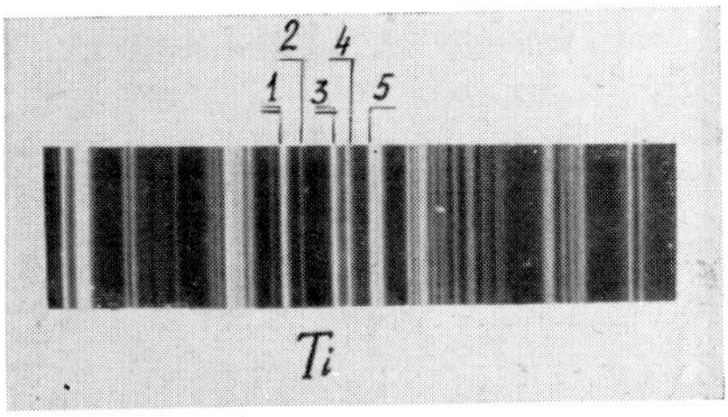

FIG. 33. Line group for determining titanium.

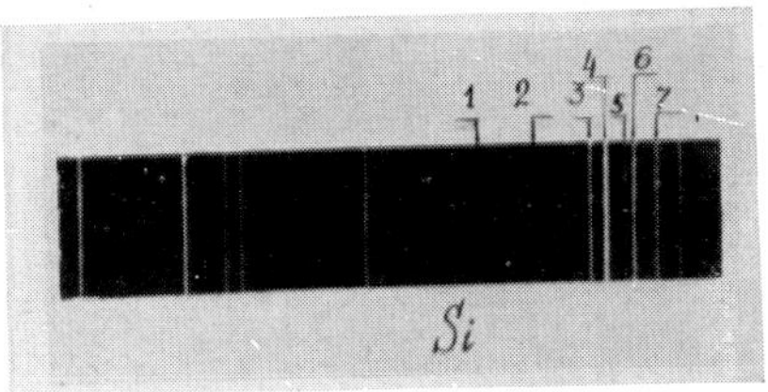

FIG. 34. Line group in red region for determining silicon.

region, where the sensitivity of the eye is a minimum. To intensity the spectrum, an arc with a current intensity of 10–20 A has to be used, but even then it is difficult to detect silicon concentrations below 0·8 per cent.

In practice the group in the red region (Fig. 34) is used. The silicon lines 6347·0 and 6371·1 Å do not appear in the arc, and therefore the following excitation regime has to be employed: an IG-2 (IG-3) generator and a voltage in the primary circuit of the step-up transformer of 220 V, current 3·5–4 A. The capacitance of the discharge circuit is 0·02 μF, the self-inductance is 0·01 mH. The permanent electrode is a wedge-shaped copper bar. For 60–90 sec a sharp fall in the brightness of the silicon lines is observed. Therefore in analysing steels the relative intensity of the lines is determined without any preliminary sparking. The wavelengths of the analysis lines and the comparison criteria are given in Table 10. Experience, and daily control of the results through the analysis of specimens with known content of silicon, are essential prerequisites for silicon determination.

TABLE 10. SPECTRAL LINES AND CRITERIA FOR EVALUATING SILICON

Wavelength, in Å	Provisional numeration of lines	Content of silicon, %	Ratio of line intensities
Si 6347·0	*1*	0·1–0·15	$1 \leq 5$
Si 6371·1	*2*	0·3	$1 = 7$
Fe 6393·6	*3*	0·6	$1 = 3$; $2 = 5$
Fe 6400·0	*4*	1·1–1·2	$1 > 3$
Fe 6408·0	*5*	1·2–1·4	$1 > 3$; $1 \leq 4$
Fe 6411·7	*6*	1·8–2·0	$1 \geq 4$; $2 < 3$
Fe 6421·4	*7*	3·0–4·0	$1 > 7$

9. Copper is determined through excitation of a spectrum by a low-frequency spark produced by a PS-39 generator with connexion of an extra 40-μF capacitor.[30] The spark supply current is 5 A, and the permanent elec-

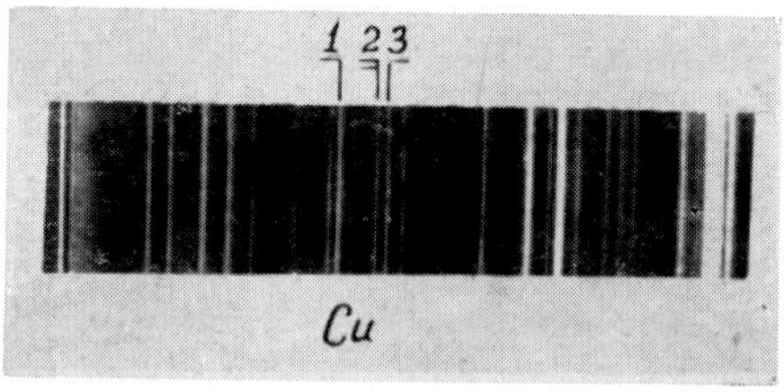

FIG. 35. Line group for determining copper in steel.

trode is a wedge-shaped carbon electrode. The analysis gap length is 1 mm. Under these conditions the spectrum is slightly weaker than in the case of excitation by an a.c. arc, but the lines are more sensitive to variations in the concentration of copper. With the proposed method it is possible to assess copper contents of 0·05 per cent and more. The line Cu 5105·5 Å (*2*) is compared with the iron lines 5098·7 Å (*1*) and 5107·5 Å (*3*) shown in Fig. 35. Table 11 gives the comparison criteria. In view of the special characteristics of the sparks of the copper lines, with sufficient experience it is also possible to determine intermediate concentrations for which no data are given in Table 11.

TABLE 11. SPECTROSCOPIC CRITERIA FOR EVALUATING COPPER

Content of copper, %	Ratio of line intensities
0·05–0·1	$2 \leqslant 3$ and does not spark
0·1 –0·15	$2 \leqslant 3$ and sparks infrequently
0·20	$2 = 3$
0·25–0·30	$2 > 3$; $2 < 1$
0·30–0·35	$2 \geqslant 3$; $2 \geqslant 1$

10. It is difficult to evaluate aluminium in steel. The aluminium lines 3944·0 and 3961·5 Å excited in the arc are located in the marginal violet region, which is very unfavourable for visual photometry. There is no guarantee that reliable semi-quantitative analyses can be made. But in most cases a qualitative analysis will suffice, that simply establishes whether the spectrum of the steel does or does not contain aluminium lines. The two lines mentioned can be detected by first looking at the spectrum of aluminium and then the spectrum of the analysis specimen.

6. GRADING COPPER-BASE ALLOYS BY MEANS OF A SPECTROSCOPE

The composition of copper-base alloys varies considerably. The main consituents, in addition to copper, may include zinc, tin, lead, manganese, nickel, aluminium, silicon and other elements. If there are pronounced quantitative, or even better, pronounced qualitative differences in the composition of the specimens, then ~~the~~ they can easily be graded by means of a spectroscope. For such cases, in particular, the use is recommended of the procedures described in this section of the present book. Their accuracy is not high. Grades of alloys very similar in composition to each other cannot be distinguished by means of a spectroscope.

The main cause of the difficulties encountered in carrying out accurate spectral analysis of copper alloys is that a change in the concentration of one of the elements alters the intensity of the lines of the other elements. This phenomenon is known as the "third-body" effect. The line intensities of the other elements silicon, tin, phosphorus, nickel and manganese in particular undergo considerable distortion.

The spectra of copper alloys do not contain many lines and thus the choice of the analysis pairs is difficult. This factor underlies the second reason for the inaccuracy of spectral analysis of the elements in copper alloys. On the other hand, the presence of a small number of lines in the spectrum makes it easier to identify the spectrum.

An a.c. arc is used to excite the lines of zinc, tin, lead, nickel, manganese and iron. The current intensity using an SL–11–4a spectroscope, is 8-10 A.

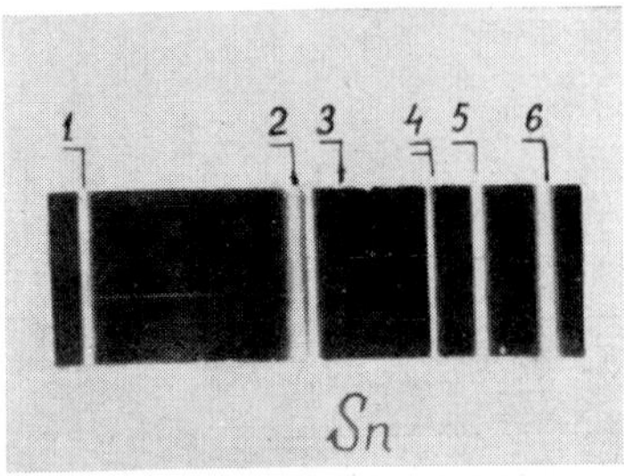

FIG. 36. Line group in indigo region for determining tin in copper alloys.

The reason for the higher current intensity compared with that used in steel analysis, is the need to increase the brightness of the spectrum. The intensity of the copper lines is also raised through the use of a copper permanent electrode. The permanent electrode should be note less than 10–15 mm in diameter, and its end should be hemispherical or wedge-shaped. Disc electrodes should not be thinner than 2 mm. The analysis gap length is 2–3 mm.

The spectroscopic criteria for the grading of copper alloys, are taken from Sventitskii's book.[(4)] A more accurate rapid analysis of bronzes and brasses can be carried out on an SL-11 spectroscope using the photometric wedge (cf. Section 8).

1. Contents of tin above 0·1 per cent can be determined from lines in the indigo region of the spectrum (Fig. 36). Table 12 gives the line wavelengths, the provisional numeration of the lines and the comparison criteria. On the basis of the tin content it is simple to distinguish tin brasses from brasses of other grades and tin bronzes, and also to sort the bronzes BrOF 6·5–0·4 and BrOF 10–1, etc.

2. Table 13 gives criteria for determining the concentrations of zinc, and the wavelengths of the line pairs. The relevant part of the spectrum is shown in Fig. 37. On the basis of the zinc content it is not difficult to determine to which grade of the simple brasses: L96, L90, L85, L80, L70, (L68, L66), etc., a specimen belongs.

The data given in Table 13 are valid for alloys not containing tin. An increase in the concentration of tin in an alloy leads to a rise in the figure obtained

TABLE 12. SPECTRAL LINES AND CRITERIA FOR EVALUATING TIN

Wavelength in Å	Provisional numeration of lines	Ratio of line intensities	Content of tin, %
Cu 4480·4	*1*	*4=3*	0·1
Cu 4507·5	*2*	*4≥3*	0·2
Cu 4513·2	*3*	*4=2; 4<6*	0·6
Sn 4524·7	*4*	*4≥2; 4≤6*	1
Cu 4530·8	*5*	*4=6; 4>2*	1·5
Cu 4539·7	*6*	*4=1*	2
		4=5	6
		4≥5	8
		4>5	10

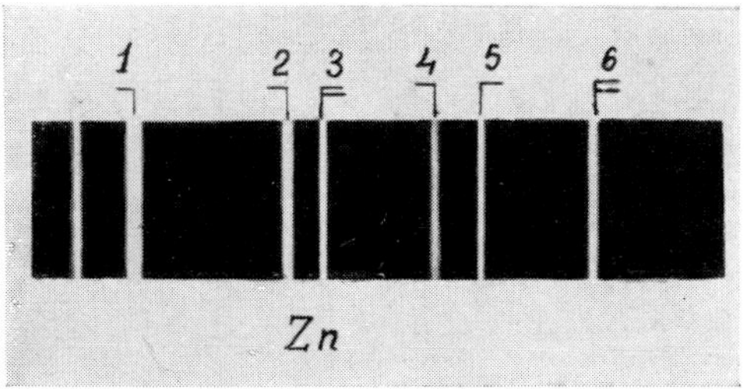

FIG. 37. Line group in blue region for determining zinc in copper alloys.

TABLE 13. SPECTRAL LINES AND CRITERIA FOR EVALUATING ZINC

Wavelength in Å	Provisional numeration in lines	Ratio of line intensities	Content of zinc, %
Cu 4651·1	*1*	*6≤4*	0·1
Cu 4674·8	*2*	*6<5; 6=4*	0·5
Zn 4680·1	*3*	*6≤5; 6=2*	1·0
Cu 4697·5	*4*	*6≥5; 3=2*	1·5
Cu 4704·6	*5*	*3>2; 3=5*	5
Zn 4722·2	*6*	*3>5; 6≥1*	10
		3=1; 6>1	12
		3≥1	15
		3>1	20
		3≫1	greater than 30

when evaluating the zinc content. Thus, for a specimen containing 4–5 per cent of zinc and about 6 per cent of tin, the ratio between the intensities of the zinc and copper lines is the same as that for a binary alloy containing 10–12 per cent of zinc.

3. The content of lead can be determined roughly by comparing the lines Pb 5005·4 Å (*1*) and Cu 5016·6 Å (*2*). Table 14 gives the ratio of the intensities of these lines for various concentrations of lead. Lead brasses and OTsS bronzes can be distinguished from other copper-base alloys on the basis of whether lead is present; on the basis of the content of lead it is possible to distinguish LS60–1 (LS59–1) and LS64–2 (LS63–3) brasses.

TABLE 14. SPECTROSCOPIC CRITERIA FOR EVALUATING LEAD

Ratio of line intensities	Content of lead, %
1 hardly visible	0·5
$1 \ll 2$	1
$1 < 2$	2
$1 \leqslant 2$	4
$1 = 2$	6
$1 > 2$	8
$1 \gg 2$	30

4. Manganese is used as an alloying element in alloys of grades BrMts5, BrAMts9–2, BrKMts3–1, BrAZhMts10–3–1·5, LMts58–2, LMtsA57–3–1,

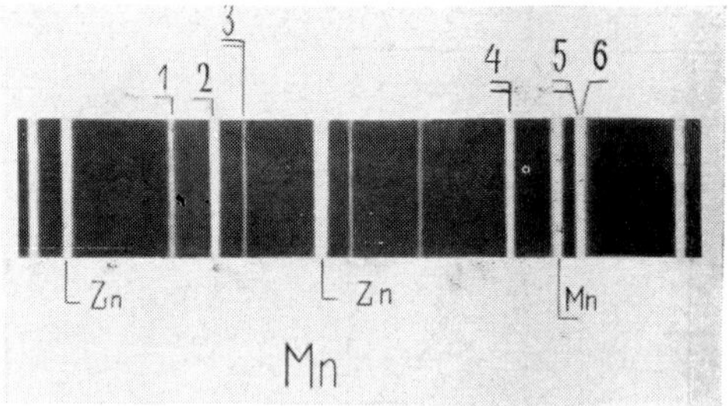

FIG. 38. Line group in blue region for determining manganese in copper alloys.

etc. The content of manganese in these alloys is determined on the basis of the group of lines in the blue region of the spectrum (Fig. 38), the wavelengths and the intensity ratios of which are given in Table 15.

5. Figure 39 illustrates the position of the lines used to determine contents of nickel (green region). Table 16 gives the comparison data. The lower limit of the nickel concentrations that can be determined (0·5 per cent) is charac-

TABLE 15. SPECTRAL LINES AND CRITERIA FOR EVALUATING MANGANESE

Wavelength in Å	Provisional numeration of lines	Ratio of line intensities	Content of manganese, %
Cu 4697·5	*1*	*4<1; 5=6*	0·2
Cu 4704·6	*2*	*4=1; 4<2*	0·5
Mn 4709·7	*3*	*4=2*	1
Mn 4754·0	*4*	*4>2; 3≥1*	2
Mn 4766·4	*5*	*3=2*	4
Cu 4766·7	*6*	*3≥2*	6
		3>2	10

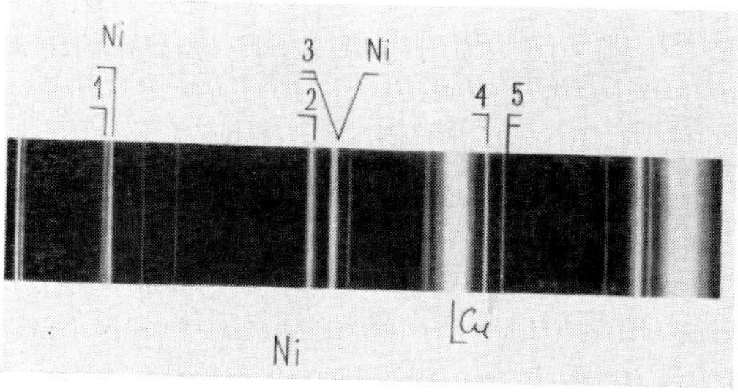

FIG. 39. Line group in green region for determining nickel in copper alloys.

teristic of most manganese and aluminium bronzes, with the exception of type BrAZhN10–4–4 aluminium–iron–nickel bronzes. The nickel content of type BrKNO5–2 bronzes and LAN 59–3–2 and LN65–5 brasses, is higher.

TABLE 16. SPECTRAL LINES AND CRITERIA FOR EVALUATING NICKEL

Wavelength in Å	Provisional numeration of lines	Ratio of line intensities	Content of nickel, %
Cu 5034·3	*1*	*3≪2*	0·5
Cu 5076·2	*2*	*3<2; 5<4*	1
Ni 5080·5	*3*	*3=1*	2
Cu 5111·9	*4*	*3≤2; 5<4*	2·5
Ni 5115·4	*5*	*3=2*	3
		3≥2; 5≤4	4
		5=4	5
		3>2; 5≥4	6

6. Iron contents of 0·1 per cent or above can be determined from lines in the indigo region (Fig. 40), the wavelengths and the intensity ratios of which are given in Table 17.

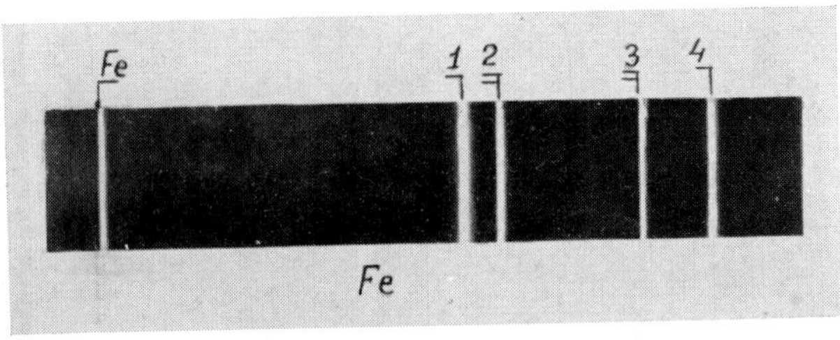

FIG. 40. Line group in indigo region for determining iron in copper alloys.

TABLE 17. SPECTRAL LINES AND CRITERIA FOR EVALUATING IRON

Wavelength in Å	Provisional numeration of lines	Ratio of line intensities	Content of iron, %
Cu 4378·2	*1*	*2*<*4*	0·1
Fe 4383·5	*2*	*2*=*4*	0·2
Fe 4404·8	*3*	*2*⩽*1*	0·5
Cu 4415·6	*4*	*2*=*1*	0·8
		2⩾*1*: *3*⩽*1*	1
		3=*4*	2
		3>*1*	4
		3≫*1*	6

Tin bronzes contain less than 0·4 per cent of iron. Simple brasses, and manganese and many aluminium brasses contain not more than 0·3 per cent of iron. The content of iron is greater in the following well-known copper-base commercial alloys: LAZh 60–1–1, LZhMts 59–1–1, LMts 58–2, LMtsA 57–3–1 LAZhMts 66–6–3–2, BrAZh9–4, BrAZhMts, BrAZhN. Some of these alloys can be distinguished simply by determining their iron content.

7. The silicon content can be determined approximately on the basis of lines in the red region of the spectrum. The conditions for excitation of the spectrum are the same as those for the determination of silicon in steels. The same parts of the spectrum are used (Fig. 34), because an iron electrode is used as the permanent electrode. The wavelengths of the lines and the comparison data are given in Table 18.

Silicon and silicon–lead brasses, silicon–nickel and silicon–manganese bronzes can be distinguished on the basis of the content of silicon. Different

TABLE 18. SPECTRAL LINES AND CRITERIA FOR EVALUATING SILICON

Wavelength in Å	Provisional numeration in lines	Ratio of line intensities	Content of silicon, %
Si 6347·0	*1*	*1*≤*5*	1
Si 6371·1	*2*	*1*>*5*; *1*≤*7*	2
Fe 6393·6	*3*	*1* = *3*	4
Fe 6400·0	*4*	*1* = *4*	5
Fe 6408·0	*5*		
Fe 6411·7	*6*		
Fe 6421·4	*7*		

grades of these alloys can usually be distinguished by determining the content of silicon and other elements.

8. In grading tin–phosphorus bronzes it is an advantage to determine the phosphorus content. With a DG-1 or DG-2 generator under the spark regime (for a spectroscope), phosphorus lines can be excited in the orange region of the spectrum. The current intensity of the spark is 3A, the transformer feed current is 0·4A, the length of the auxiliary (discharge) gap is 1 mm and that of the analysis gap 2 mm. Pure nickel wedge-shaped electrodes with a working surface of 2 mm in diameter, are used as the permanent electrodes.(31)

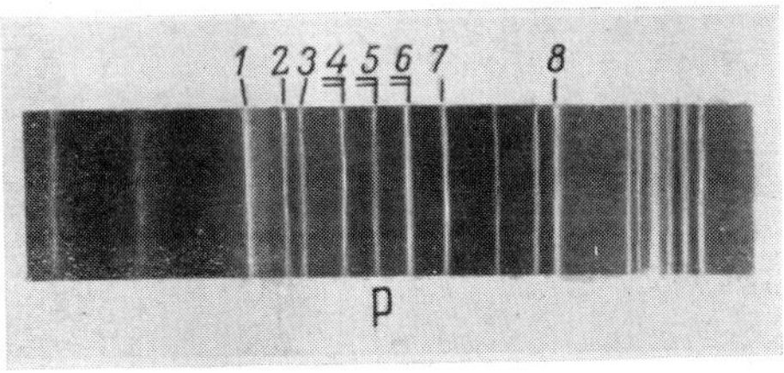

FIG. 41. Line group in orange region for determining phosphorus in copper alloys.

The phosphorus and nickel line pairs (Fig. 41) are located in the area of the third group of manganese, used to analyse steel. The wavelengths of the lines and comparison data for evaluating phosphorus, are given in Table 19.

9. Bronzes of grades BrAL5, BrAL7, BrAZh9–4, BrAMts9–2, BrAZhMts 10–3–1·5 and BrAZhN10–4–4, can easily be distinguished by determining whether their spectra contain aluminium lines. They can be further graded on the basis of whether or not they contain iron, manganese or nickel lines. The only grades that cannot be distinguished are grades BrAL5 and BrAL7. In most cases the presence of the arc lines of aluminium 3944·0 and 3961·5 Å

TABLE 19. SPECTRAL LINES AND CRITERIA FOR EVALUATING PHOSPHORUS

Wavelength in Å	Provisional numeration of lines	Ratio of line intensities	Content of phosphorus, %
Ni 5996·7	*1*	*6*<*2*; *4*—separate sparks	0·05
Ni 6007·3	*2*	*6* = *2*; *4* < *2*	0·12
Ni 6012·2	*3*	*6*≥*3*; *5*—separate sparks	0·30
P 6024·1	*4*	*6* < *7*; *5* < *2*; *4* = *3*	0.55
P 6033·9	*5*	*6* = *7*; *5* ≤ *2*	0·65
P 6043·0	*6*	*6* = *1*; *4* = *7*; *5* ≥ *2*	0·80
Ni 6053·7	*7*	*6* = *8*	1·00
Ni 6086·3	*8*		

is determined. They can be seen at a high arc current intensity (8–12A). The regime proposed for determining silicon in copper alloys, will excite the spark line of aluminium Al 5696·5 Å. This line is poorly visible at aluminium concentrations of 0·6–0·8 per cent, and clearly visible at aluminium concentrations exceeding 2 per cent.

7. GRADING OF ALUMINIUM- AND MAGNESIUM-BASE ALLOYS

The most commonly-used aluminium- and magnesium-base alloys differ as regards the combination of elements that they contain. Thus, the alloy AL2 contains silicon in addition to aluminium; AL4 contains slightly less silicon, and also magnesium and manganese. Alloy AL5 contains silicon, magnesium and copper, while of these elements alloy AL7 contains only copper. Characteristic qualitative features of other grades of alloys can also be distinguished. In this way, in grading light metals use can be made of whether or not the spectrum contains lines of specific elements, and only a very rough estimate of their content need be made.(32)

The spectrum is excited by an a.c. arc. The arc current is 2–4 A, the permanent electrode being pure aluminium. An Armco iron electrode is used to detect nickel. Silicon in aluminium alloys, and also aluminium, zinc and manganese in magnesium alloys, are determined with an electrode of electrolytic copper. The length of the analysis gap is set by a gauge at 2 mm. Small parts and specimens should not be used because they will evaporate strongly, thus producing sharp variations in the line intensities. To avoid melting the specimens, the arc must be switched off periodically.

Table 20 gives lines for determining the presence in an alloy of silicon, copper, magnesium, manganese, nickel, zinc and aluminium. The ease of detection and brightness of the lines depends on the type of spectroscope used and on

TABLE 20. SPECTRAL LINES USED TO GRADE ALUMINIUM AND MAGNESIUM ALLOYS

Element	Spectral line wavelengths, Å	Estimation of content
Silicon	6347·0 6371·1	At 1% the line 6347 Å is hardly visible; at 5% it is clearly visible; at 10% it is more intense, and line 6371 Å appears.
Copper	5105·5 5153·2 5218·2 5292·5 5700·2 5782·1	At 0·15–0·20% all the lines except 5700 Å are visible; line 5700 Å is clearly visible at 1·5–2·5%; at 4–5% lines 5105, 5153, 5218 Å are very bright.
Manganese	4754·0 4761·5 4766·4 4783·4 4823·5	
Magnesium	5167·3 5172·7 5183·6	At contents <0·1% these lines are hardly visible; all three lines are clearly visible at 0·2–0·4%, but they are not intense; at 1·5–2% the lines are fairly bright, and at 6–10% they are very bright.
Nickel	5080·5 5081·1	
Aluminium	3944·0 3961·5	
Zinc	4680·1 4722·2 4810·5 6362·3	At contents <0·1% these lines are only very poorly visible.

the specific conditions of operation of the light source. Thus in cases where the content of an element is estimated on the basis of the line intensities, the criteria listed should be checked and compared with spectra of specimens of known composition.

During the analysis process all the elements are determined in turn. On the basis of the combination of the criteria (Table 21) it is usually not difficult to determine the grade of alloy to which the test-piece belongs. Difficulties

TABLE 21. SPECTRAL LINES FOR GRADING ALUMINIUM- AND MAGNESIUM-BASE ALLOYS

Aloy	Si	Cu	Mn	Mg	Ni	Al	Zn
Aluminium	–	–	–	–	–	+++	–
AL2	++	–	–	–	–	+++	–
AL4	++	–	+	+	–	+++	–
AL5	+	+	–	+	–	+++	–
AL7	–	++	–	–	–	+++	–
AL8	–	–	–	+++	–	+++	–
AL9	+	–	–	+	–	+++	–
AL10	+	+++	–	+	–	+++	+++
AL11	+	–	–	–	–	+++	+++
AK2	–	++	–	+	+	+++	–
AK4	–	+	–	++	+	+++	–
AK5	–	+	+	+	–	+++	–
AK6	–	+	++	+	–	+++	–
AK8	–	++	++	+	–	+++	–
D16	–	++	++	++	–	+++	–
Magnesium	–	–	–	+++	–	–	–
ML4	–	–	+	+++	–	+	++
ML5	–	–	+	+++	–	++	+
ML6	–	–	+	+++	–	++	++

Notation: – lines absent or flashing periodically
+ lines of element present
++ bright lines
+++ lines very bright

are encountered only in distinguishing alloys very similar in composition to each other, e.g. AL4 and AL9, ML4 and ML6.

In addition to grading light metals, it is also often necessary to determine rapidly the content of the individual elements therein. This is particularly the case in the control of casting operations. Experience in a large number of works has confirmed the suitability of spectroscopy for this purpose.

At the spectral analysis laboratory of the Electric Motor Works at Mogilev a spectroscopic analysis is carried out at 30–40 min intervals, of the metal in the crucibles, to determine their iron, copper and silicon contents. The results of the spectroscopic determinations are checked periodically (at 1–1·5 hr intervals) by means of quantitative spectrographic analysis methods. Spectroscopists very rarely obtain erroneous results in determining whether or not an alloy satisfies technical requirements.

Iron and copper are determined in the spectroscope through excitation of the spectrum by an a.c. arc ($I = 4$A). In determining iron, a copper permanent electrode, and in determining copper, an iron permanent electrode is used. In both cases the electrodes are wedge-shaped, or metallic discs. It is particularly important to keep constant the length of the analysis gap (2–2·5 mm) and the shape of the permanent electrode. Thus, if the gap length increases whilst determining iron, the results obtained will be on the low side.

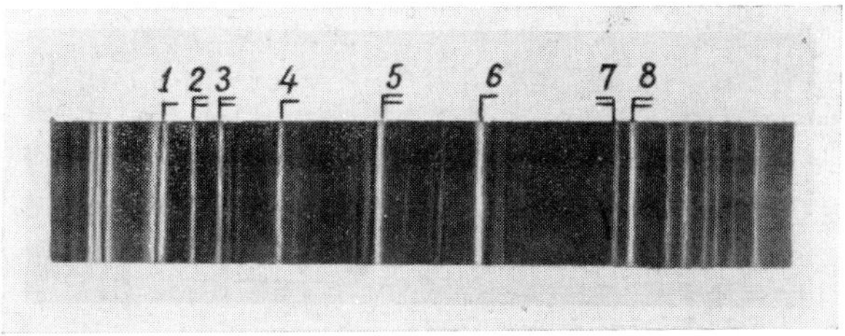

FIG. 42. Line group in green region for determining iron in aluminium alloys.

The iron content is determined on the basis of lines in the green region of the spectrum. The comparison criteria given in Refs. 4 and 20 have been supplemented somewhat in the works laboratory. Figure 42 illustrates the position of the lines in a group, and their wavelengths and intensity ratios are given in Table 22.

TABLE 22. SPECTRAL LINES AND CRITERIA FOR EVALUATING IRON

Wavelengths, Å	Provisional numeration of lines	Ratio of line intensities	Content of iron, %
Cu 5220·1	*1*	*5* = *4*; line *2* not visible on background of molecular spectrum	0·2
Fe 5227·2	*2*		
Fe 5232·9	*3*		
Cu 5245·4	*4*	$5 \geqslant 4;\ 2 < 4$	0·3
Fe 5269·5	*5*	$5 > 4;\ 2 \leqslant 4$	0·5
Cu 5292·5	*6*	$2 = 4$	0·7
Fe 5324·2	*7*	$2 \geqslant 4;\ 5 \leqslant 6$	1·0
Fe 5328·0	*8*	$2 > 4;\ 5 \leqslant 6;\ 8 < 6$	1 2–1·3
		$8 \geqslant 6;\ 8 < 1;\ 5 < 6$	1.5–1·6
		$8 > 1;\ 5 \geqslant 1;\ 5 \leqslant 6$	1·9–2·0
		$2 \gg 4;\ 5 > 6$	>2·0

Copper is determined on the basis of the criteria given in Table 23, while the working part of the spectrum is shown in Fig. 43.

TABLE 23. SPECTRAL LINES AND CRITERIA FOR EVALUATING COPPER

Names of groups of lines	Wavelengths, Å	Provisional numeration of lines	Content of copper, %	Ratio of intensities of lines in groups	
				Cu_1	Cu_2
	Fe 5097·0	1	0·05	2 ≥ 5	
	Cu 5105·5	*2*	1·0	2 = *1*	
	Fe 5107·4	*3*	0·2	2 = 4	
Cu_1	Fe 5110·4	*4*	0·5	2 = 3	
	Fe 5121·6	*5*	1	2 > *3*	*4 = 3*
	Fe 5142·5	*6*	2		*4 > 3; 4 < 5*
			4	2 = 6	*4 ≤ 5; 4 ≤ 1*
	Fe 5273·2	*1*	6		*4 = 1*
	Fe 5281·8	*2*	10		*4 = 5*
	Fe 5287·9	*3*	>15%		*4 > 5*
Cu_2	Cu 5292·5	*4*			
	Fe 5302·3	*5*			
	Fe 5324·2	*6*			

Silicon in aluminium alloys is assessed by the procedure described in Ref. 33. The light source is a low-voltage spark with the following parameters: capacitance of discharge circuit 25 μF, inductance about 75 μH, transformer

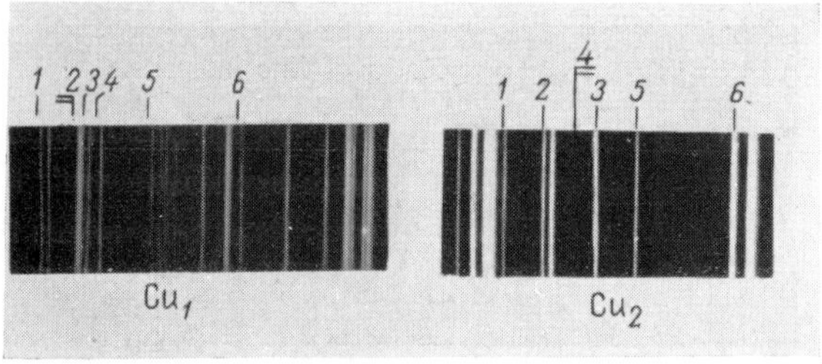

FIG. 43. Line group in green region for determining copper in aluminium alloys.

feed current 0·7 A, current intensity in arc circuit 6 A. The length of the gap between the electrodes is 0·8–1 mm. The permanent electrode is of iron. A similar low-voltage spark regime can be obtained with a DG-1 (DG-2) generator. Analysis is carried out by comparing the red spark lines of silicon with the iron lines. The wavelengths of the analysis lines and the comparison criteria are given in Table 24. The part of the spectrum differs little from that given in Fig. 34, in connexion with the determination of silicon in steel.

TABLE 24. SPECTRAL LINES AND CRITERIA FOR EVALUATING SILICON

Wavelengths, Å	Provisional numeration of lines	Ratio of line intensities	Content of silicon, %
Al 6243·4	Al	*1* < *5*	0·15–0·20
Si 6347·0	*1*	*1* ⩽ *5*	0·20–0·30
Si 6371·1	*2*	*1* = *5*	0·40–0·50
Fe 6393·6	*3*	*1* = *7*; *2* ⩽ *5*	0·7
Fe 6400·0	*4*	*1* = *6*; *2* ⩾ *5*; *2* ⩽ *7*	1·0
Fe 6408·0	*5*	*1* ⩾ *6*; *1* = *3*; *2* = *7*	1·3
Fe 6411·7	*6*	*1* ⩽ *4*; *2* ⩽ *3*	1·7
Fe 6421·4	*7*	*2* = *3*	2–2·5
		1 = *4*; *2* ⩾ *3*	4–4·5
		1 ⩽ Al	6–7
		1 = Al; *2* = *4*	8–10
		1 ⩾ Al; *2* > *4*	15
		2 = Al	20

8. ANALYSIS WITH AN SL-11 SPECTROSCOPE BY MEANS OF A PHOTOMETRIC WEDGE

When a photometric wedge is used it is no longer necessary to take a large number of analysis pairs. The line of the comparison impurity is compared with an adjacent line of the element of the parent metal. The brighter line of the two is set against the wedge. The introduction of the wedge lowers the intensity of the line to that of the second line of the analysis pair. After the intensities of these line have been made equal, the divisions of the scale are read off. The figure thereby obtained gives the intensity of the non-attenuated line, as a percentage of the intensity of the attenuated line. Thus, the readings of the photometric wedge characterize the relative intensity of the lines of the analysis pair, and depend on the content of the element being determined in the specimen. This relation can be expressed graphically if standard specimens of known chemical composition are available. The standard specimens issued by scientific research centres in the U.S.S.R. can be used, or else specimens of commercial alloys that have been selected must be analysed in two or three other laboratories as well.

In selecting standards, efforts should be made to see that their chemical composition resembles that of the test-pieces, and that the contents in the

TABLE 25. ALLOY ANALYSIS CONDITIONS FOR AN SL-11 SPECTROSCOPE FITTED WITH A PHOTOMETRIC WEDGE

Type of alloy	Element being determined	Range of concentrations	Wavelengths of analysis line pairs, Å	Light source regime
1	2	3	4	5
Steels and cast irons	Mn	0·2–2·0	Mn 4783·4 – Fe 4789·6	Arc: $I = 4$ A, permanent electrode a copper disc 1·5–2 mm thick; analysis gap 2·5 mm. Heating time 20 sec.
	Cr	0·01–0·5	Cr 5204·5 } Cr 5206·0 } – Fe 5202·3	
	Cr	0·3–5·0	Cr 5345·8 – Fe 5341·0	
	Cr	6–20	Cr 5348·3 – Fe 5341·0	
	Cr	ditto	Cr 4922·3 – Fe 4919·0	
	W	1–18	W 5053·3 – Fe 5049·8	
	V	0·1–0·7	V 4379·2 – Fe 4375·9	
	V	0·5–3·0	V 4875·5 – Fe 4878·2	
	Ni	0·4–2·0	Ni 4714·4 – Fe 4707·3	
	Mo	0·1–1·5	Mo 5533·0 – Fe 5501·5	
	Ti	0·1–1·0	Ti 4991·1 – Fe 5001·9	
	Si	0·8–4·0	Si 6347·0 – Fe 6400·0	Low-voltage spark: $I = 4$ A, permanent electrode a copper disc, analysis gap 2 mm. Sparking time 60 sec.
		0·5–6·0	Si 6347·0 – Cu 6325·4	

1	2	3	4	5
Copper-base alloys	Sn	0·5 – 10	Sn 4524·7 – Cu 4530·8	Arc: $I = 4$ A, permanent electrode a copper disc 1·5–2 mm thick, analysis gap 2·5 mm. Heating time 20–40 sec.
	Zn	0·1 – 10	Zn 4722·2 – Cu 4704·6	
	Pb	3 – 30	Pb 5005·4 – Cu 5016·6	
	Ni	0·5 – 5·0	Ni 4714·4 – Cu 4704·6	
	Mn	0·5 – 6·0	Mn 4709·7 – Cu 4704·6	
	Fe	0·2 – 2·0	Fe 4383·6 – Cu 4378·2	
	Fe	1 – 6·0	Fe 5232·9 – Cu 5245·4	
Aluminium-base alloys	Cu	0·2 – 2·0	Cu 5105·5 – Fe 5110·4	Arc: $I = 2$ A, permanent electrode of Armco iron, analysis gap 2 mm.
	Cu	2 – 10	Cu 5292·5 – Fe 5302·3	
	Mg	0·1 – 2·0	Mg 5172·7 – Fe 5168·9	
	Mg	0·2 – 2·0	Mn 4783·4 – Fe 4789·6	Permanent electrode copper, other conditions the same as for copper and magnesium.
	Zn	0·2 – 3·0	Zn 6362·3 – Fe 6393·6	
	Fe	0·4 – 3·0	Fe 5283·6 – Cu 5292·5	
	Si	1 – 15	Si 6371·1 – Fe 6393·6	Low-voltage spark: $I = 2$ A, permanent electrode of Armco iron

specimens of the elements being determined lie within the limits of variation in the concentrations of these elements in the standards.

The choice of the line pairs should be based on the following considerations:

1. The intensity of the line of the element being determined should vary appreciably with the concentration of this element in the sample, i.e. the line should have a high concentration sensitivity.

2. The analysis line pairs must be homologous, of identical sharpness and free from superimposition of lines of other elements.

There are a number of analysis line pairs which have been tried out in spectroscopic analysis (cf. Section 10). However many of these pairs are unsuitable for use with a spectroscope, because the lines are some distance from each other. The SL-11 spectroscope does not contain a device for bringing the lines closer together.

Table 25 lists the line pairs that we have used in the analysis of copper-, iron- and aluminium-base alloys by means of an SL-11 spectroscope. The last column gives the basic conditions of excitation of the spectrum.

In analysing copper- and aluminium-base alloys, lines of the material of the permanent electrode are used as the internal standard lines. Thus careful supervision of the shape of the electrodes and of the length of the analysis gap is necessary, because variation in the rate of feed of the electrodes may increase the analysis error.

Copper permanent electrodes should not contain more than 0·1 per cent of zinc, and 0·2 per cent of tin and iron. The contents of manganese and silicon in iron electrodes should not exceed 0·1–0·15 per cent. Electrodes of Armco iron are mostly used.

The determination of each element in the test-piece is carried out as follows. For each of four or five standards the relative intensity is measured for the analysis pair selected. The measurements are taken as the mean of 30 to 50 readings. This number of readings is obtained as a result of three to four repeated settings of each standard.

If the concentration of the element being determined varies within wide limits, then the intensity of the comparison line will have to be lowered in the case of some standards, and that of the standard line in the case of other standards. As a result of this change in the line attenuation the results have to be converted. When it is the intensity of the standard line that is lowered, 100 is subtracted from the reading obtained from the photometric wedge. When it is the intensity of the comparison line that is lowered, the readings of the wedge must be subtracted from 100. A graph is plotted on the basis of the converted values thus obtained. The values of the concentration of the element in the standards (in per cent) are plotted along the axis as abscissae.

The corresponding readings of the wedge are plotted along the axis as ordinates. By drawing a smooth graph through the points thus obtained, we get a calibration curve. In subsequent work it is used to determine the content of the element in question in the test-pieces.

Figure 44 shows a calibration curve for determining manganese in low-alloy steels. The line pair used was Mn4783·4–Fe 4789·6 Å. At a manganese content of 0·25 per cent the line Fe 4789·6 Å was attenuated, in the other cases the line Mn 4783·4 Å.

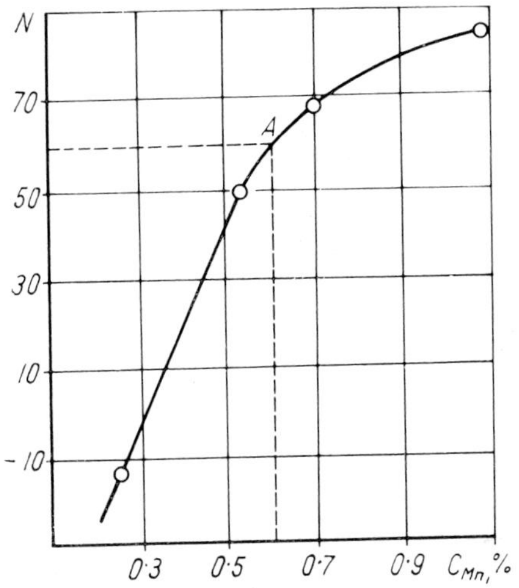

FIG. 44. Calibration curve for determining manganese by means of a photometric wedge using an SL-11 spectroscope. Concentrations of manganese in standards plotted along horizontal axis, relative intensity of analysis pair along vertical axis.

The readings of the wedge obtained for the test-pieces are based as before on five to ten measurements (usually at a single setting of the test-pieces) and are converted like those of the standards.

Let us suppose for instance that a reading of 40 per cent is obtained for the test-pieces. The comparison line is then attenuated. After conversion we get 100—40 per cent = 60 per cent. To this value of the ordinate in Fig. 44. there corresponds the point A. Dropping a vertical from this point, we find the required concentration along the axis of the abscissae (0·61 per cent).

A separate calibration curve is drawn for each element. The graphs plotted for one type of alloy should not be used to analyse other alloys of very different chemical composition. For example, it is impossible to determine manganese in low-alloy steels and steels of the YalT type or cast-irons, from a single calibration graph.

Each spectroscopist should plot his own calibration curves and use them in his daily work. The procedure for checking the position of the graph is described briefly in the following section.

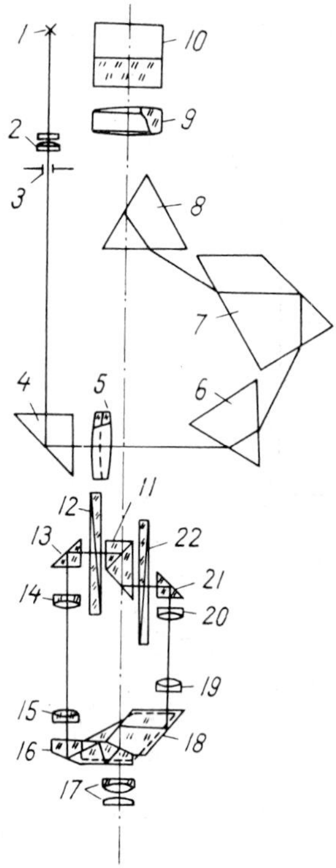

FIG. 45. Optical design of ST-7 spectrometer (plan view).

1—light source; *2*—condenser; *3*—spectral slit of spectrometer; *4*—right angle prism; *5*—collimator objective; *6, 7, 8*—dispersing system of prisms; *9*—objective of telescope; *10*—right angle prism; *11*—complex prism with silvered faces *ab* and *ac*; *12* and *22*—photometric wedges; *13* and *21*—rotary prisms; *14, 15* and *19, 20*—turning lenses; *16* and *18*—prisms for combining the parts of the spectra and directing them along the optical axis; *17*—eye-piece.

9. ST-7 SPECTROMETER

A spectrometer is a spectroscope supplemented by a photometric device and designed for quantitative spectral analysis. Figure 45 illustrates the optical system of the ST-7 spectrometer. Light from the arc *1* passes through a condenser *2* and a prism *3* and is directed by the prism *4* on to the collimator objective *5*. The pencil of rays is broken into a spectrum by the dispersing prisms *6* to *8*. The spectrum is turned through 180° by the prism, and is focused by the objective of the telescope *9* in the plane passing through the centre of the hypotenuse face *ab* of the complex prism *11*. Part of the light is reflected by a narrow silvered strip applied to this face, in the direction of the left-hand photometric wedge *12*. Most of the spectrum is reflected by the face *ac* and passes through the photometric wedge 22. The two parts of the spectrum are turned by the prisms *13* and *21*, and focused by means of the turning systems *15, 14* and *19, 20* in the field of vision of the eye-piece *17*. The prisms *16* and *18* combine the two parts to produce a uniform spectrum running along the optical axis.

The observer sees a spectrum in which a small part of the spectrum is displaced vertically. The required part of the spectrum is brought into the field of view of the eye-piece by turning the knob *1* (Fig. 46). By means of the knob *4* most of the spectrum is displaced relative to the part of the spectrum enclosed in the rectangular frame. In this way it is possible to bring lines up to 400 Å apart, closer together.

In bringing the analysis pairs closer together, they are arranged so that there are no other bright lines between them to interfere with the photometry. It is advisable to carry out photometry at a constant intensity of the internal standard line. Thus the position of one wedge is fixed and equality of the intensities is achieved by moving the other wedge. On comparing bright lines, the intensity of the whole field of vision should be attenuated slightly.

In carrying out spectrometric analysis, great care should be taken to ensure that the preparation and setting of the specimens and the permanent electrodes

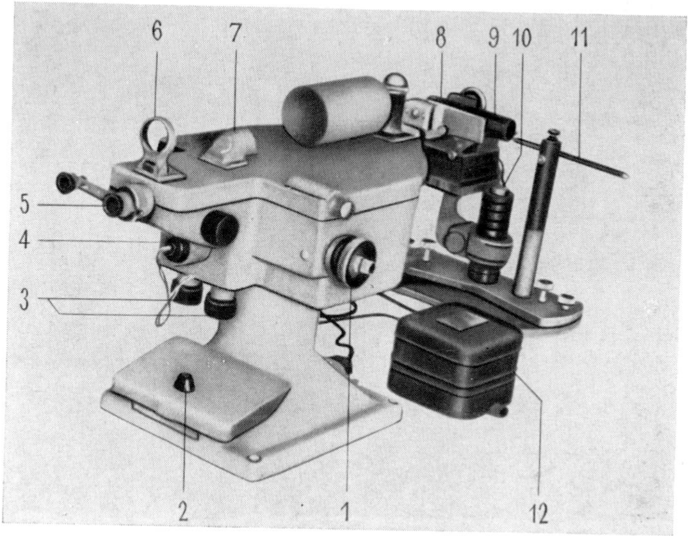

FIG. 46. External view of ST-7 spectrometer.

1—knob for turning dispersing prisms; *2*—button for connecting illumination lamp *7*; *3*—knob for moving photometric wedges and dial; *4*—knob for bringing lines together; *5*—eye-piece; *6*—lens for observation of the screen by a short-sighted observer; *8*—jaws for clamping specimen *9*; *10*—gauge; *11*—permanent electrode; *12*—transformer.

are identical. The frame holding the electrodes is fixed relative to the spectrometer by a built-in gauge. The permanent electrode is brought into contact with the gauge *10*. Then the analysis specimen *9* clamped in the jaws *8* is moved to give the prescribed analysis gap.

In making photometric determinations the recommended procedure should be adhered to very closely. During heating, the image of the entire spectrum should be focused carefully, by means of the knurled ring, and the knob located on the left-hand side of the spectrometer casing. Sharp lines can be compared more accurately.

The photometric wedges are moved by turning the knobs *3*. Scales are firmly attached to the wedges. They can be clearly seen on pressing the button

2 controlling the lamp 7. The lamp is fed with a.c. from the transformer 12. The algebraic sum of the readings on the scales characterizes the relative intensity of the analysis lines.

The relative intensity of the analysis pair, found for several specimens of known composition, is compared with the concentration of the element being determined. A linear relationship obtains when the logarithm of the concentration of the element (log *C*) is plotted against the sum of the readings on the dials (*N*). To reduce the error, five to ten readings are made for each of ten settings of the standard specimens. Thus, each point on the graph represents the result of 50 to 100 measurements.

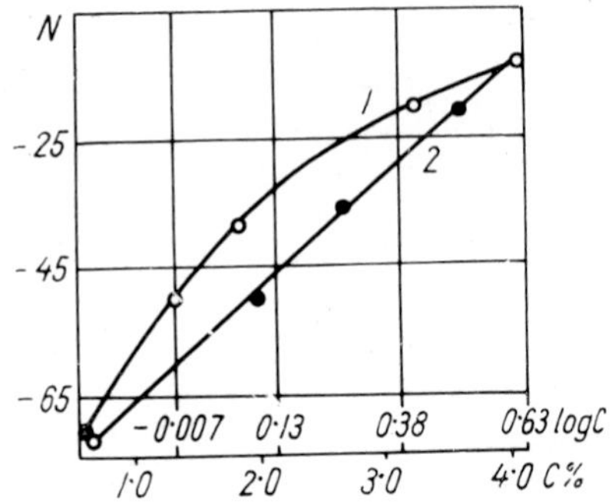

FIG. 47. Calibration curves for evaluation of chromium in steels by means of ST-7 spectrometer.

1 and *2*—respectively relationships between intensity of analysis pair Cr 5345·8 – Fe 5324·2 Å, and concentration (*C*) and logarithm of concentration (log *C*) of chromium.

Figure 47 gives calibration curves for determining chromium in steels. The straight line *2* shows the relation between *N* and log *C*. In order to obtain a linear graph three to five standards will suffice. In practice it is more convenient to plot curves correlating the concentration *C* with the relative intensity directly (curve *1*). These curves can be plotted carefully on the basis of the row of points from the corresponding rectilinear graphs (curve *2*).

It is advisable to determine the scatter of the points obtained from tenfold measurement of the relative intensity, for one of the standards with a mean concentration. In subsequent work this standard can then be used for day-to-day control of the graph constant. If the point for the control specimen is located beyond the limits of scatter of the previous results, then a working graph should be drawn through this point parallel with the main calibration curve.

As a rule the spectral sensitivity of the eye varies from person to person, and thus each observer should compile his own calibration curves.

Spectrometric determinations should be carried out in a darkened room, because the adapted eye is more sensitive to slight changes in intensity of the lines being compared.

10. ANALYSIS OF STEELS AND CAST IRONS BY MEANS OF AN ST-7 SPECTROMETER

In determining most alloying elements in steels and cast irons the spectrum is excited by an a.c. arc from a DG-1 or DG-2 generator.[34, 35] The current intensity is 4 A. The most satisfactory results are obtained with wedge-shaped copper permanent electrodes with a working area 1·5–2 mm in diameter. The length of the analysis gap is 2 mm.

The spectral line intensities can be compared more accurately when the spectrometer has a wide slit. But when the slit is very wide, adjoining lines may overlap. In addition, the background is increased noticeably. Thus the maximum permissible slit width should be determined experimentally. In the following cases it is 0·06–0·08 mm.

1. Determination of manganese is carried out on the basis of lines Mn 4823·5 Å and Fe 4859·7 Å, after heating for 20 sec. With arc excitation an intensive spectrum and a high sensitivity of the manganese line to variation in the content of manganese in the spectrum, are found. This ensures good reproducibility of the results. The analysis error at manganese concentrations of 0·3–1 per cent is 4–5 per cent of the content.

2. The analysis error is the same on determining the content of chromium in carbon and alloy steels. The analysis pair is Cr 5208·4–Fe 5227·2 Å, or Cr 5345·8–Fe 5324·2 Å. The heating time is 10–20 sec.

3. The intensity of tungsten lines rises sharply during the first seconds of arcing. Thus comparison of the lines of the analysis pair W 4843·8–Fe 4859·7 Å is carried out 40–60 sec after the arc is switched on. The analysis error is 4 per cent of the concentration being measured.

4. Molybdenum is determined from the lines Mo 5533·0 Å and Fe 5554·9 Å. The intensity of the line Mo 5533·0 Å pulsates appreciably, and therefore the photometric determination is carried out at the moment when the molybdenum line is at its brightest. The analysis error is 3–4 per cent of the content.

5. The analysis pair Ni 4714·4–Fe 4728·6 Å is used to determine nickel. Preliminary heating lasts 40 sec, the measurement time should be restricted to 1·5 min. At the end of this time the intensity of the nickel line diminishes appreciably. The other analysis conditions are as above.

6. Vanadium in high-speed steels (content 1–3 per cent) is determined by

comparing lines V 4875·5–Fe 4859·7 Å. The heating time is 40 sec. The error does not exceed 5 per cent of the content.

7. To excite silicon lines a high-voltage spark is used, because the arc spectrum does not contain spectral lines of this element suitable for analysis. The IG-3 (IG-2) generator is set to the complex connexion. The capacitance of the discharge circuit is 0·02 μF, the inductance 0·01 mH, the current intensity 3–4 A, the length of the analysis gap 2·5 mm. The permanent electrode is wedge-shaped, of electrolytic copper, with a working region 3–4 mm in diameter.

In analysing cast irons a carbon steel electrode can be used. The content of silicon in these steels is low, and they can be considered to be sufficiently pure. Experience at the spectral analysis laboratory of the Mogilev iron and steel-works has shown that reproducible results can be obtained using wedge-shaped carbon steel electrodes. The analysis pair is Si 6347·0–Fe 6301·5 Å. Sparking lasts 1·5 min.

The determination of silicon in steels where the line Si 6347·0 Å does not stand out very clearly against the background, should be carried out on the basis of a graph plotted without preliminary sparking. All the measurements should be completed in the first 20–30 sec of sparking. The permanent electrode is of copper. This results in a substantial attenuation of the line Fe 6301·5 Å, and line Fe 6400·0 Å should be used instead.

The error in determining silicon is 3–4 per cent of the content.

11. Analysis of Light Alloys Using an ST-7 Spectrometer

At the special analysis laboratory of the Mogilev iron and steel works OTsS-5-5 bronzes are analysed by the procedure described in Ref. 36. The light source in an arc (DG-2 generator) with a current intensity of 4 A; the permanent electrode is of nickel. The analysis gap is 2·5 mm, the heating time 30 sec. The slit width is 0·1 mm. The line pairs Sn 4524·7–Cu 4530·8 Å, Zn 4680·1–Cu 4674·8 Å, Pb 5005·4–Cu 5016·2 Å are used.

The intensity of the lead line pulsates sharply, therefore the measurements should be made when the line is at its brightest. The analysis error is 4—5 per cent of the content of the element being determined.

The chemical composition of other types of bronzes and brasses, aluminium-, zinc- and magnesium-base alloys, Babbits and soldering alloys can also be analysed using an ST-7 spectrometer.[34] Below in Tables 26–28 we give the analysis conditions for these alloys.

TABLE 26. CONDITIONS OF ANALYSIS OF COPPER-BASE ALLOYS

Element being determined	Wavelengths of spectral lines, Å		Light source and its basic parameters	Permanent electrode
	of element being determined	of internal standard		
Zn	Zn 4680·1	Cu 4651·1	Arc: $I = 4–5$ A	Copper
Sn	Sn 4524·7	Cu 4539·7	Arc: $I = 4–5$ A	Copper
Mn	Mn 4754·0	Cu 4704·6	Arc: $I = 4–5$ A	Copper
Ni	Ni 5080·5	Cu 5076·2	Arc: $I = 4–5$ A	Copper
Ni	Ni 4714·4	Cu 4651·1	Arc: $I = 4–5$ A	Copper
Si	Si 6347·0	Cu 6325·4	High-voltage spark: $L = 0$; $C = 0·01$ μF $I = 3$ A (simple connection)	Copper
Si	Si 6347·0	Fe 6400·0	High-voltage spark: $L = 0$; $C = 0·01$ μF; $I = 3$ A (simple connection)	Iron
Pb	Pb 5005·4	Cu 5016·6	Arc: $I = 4–5$ A	Copper
Pb	Pb 4057·8	Cu 4022·7	Arc: $I = 8–9$ A	Copper
Al	Al 5696·5	N 5666·6	High-voltage spark: $C = 0·02$ μF; $L = 0·01$ mH; $I = 3$ A (complex connection)	Copper
Fe	Fe 4383·5	Cu 4378·2	Arc: $I = 6$ A	Copper

12. ANALYSIS BASED ON THE BURNING-OUT TIME OF MATERIAL

Quantitative Analysis based on the Burning-out of Transferred Material

The visual analysis methods described above do not exhaust the possibilities of visual analysis. When a spectroscope in being used, the accuracy of the determinations can be increased by carrying out an analysis based on the burning-out of transferred material. The essence of this analysis procedure is as follows.

An arc is struck between the test-piece and a substitute electrode. The material of the substitute electrode should not contain the elements being determined. In the course of 30–60 sec of arcing, vapours of the test-piece are deposited on the face of the substitute electrode. The substitute electrode containing the layer of transferred material is then used as one of the arc (spark) electrodes. The second electrode is also made of material not containing the elements being determined. In the case of the analysis of steels, copper bars 6–8 mm in diameter and ground hemispherical at the end, can be used to deposit the vapours and during burning-out of the transferred material.

TABLE 27. CONDITIONS OF ANALYSIS OF MAGNESIUM AND ZINC ALLOYS AND BABBITS

Alloys	Element being determined	Wavelengths of spectral lines, Å		Light source and its basic parameters	Permanent electrode
		of element being determined	of internal standard		
Magnesium-base	Mn	Mn 4823·5	Fe 4859·7	High-voltage spark: $C = 0{\cdot}01\ \mu F$; $L = 0{\cdot}01$ mH; $I = 1{\cdot}5$ A (complex connexion)	Iron
	Zn	Zn 4810·5	Fe 4859·7	ditto	Iron
	Na	Na 5890·0	Fe 5914·2	ditto	Iron
Zinc-base	Pb	Pb 5608·8	N 5666·6	ditto	Copper
	Al	Al 5696·5	N 5666·6	ditto	Copper
	Cu	Cu 5218·2	Fe 5250·6	the same, $L = 0{\cdot}05$ mH	Iron
	Cu	Cu 5292·5	Fe 5287·9	ditto	Iron
	Mg	Mg 5183·6	Fe 5022·3	ditto	Iron
	Mg	Mg 5183·6	Cu 5153·2	ditto	Copper
Babbits	Cu	Cu 5153·2	Fe 5139·2	ditto	Iron
	Cu	Cu 5218·2	Fe 5250·6	ditto	Iron
	Pb	Pb 5608·8	Fe 5615·6	ditto	Iron
	Zn	Zn 4810·5	N 4803·3	ditto	Iron
	Zn	Zn 4810·5	Fe 4859·7	ditto	Iron

TABLE 28. CONDITIONS OF ANALYSIS OF ALUMINIUM-BASE ALLOYS

Element being determined	Wavelengths of spectral lines Å		Light source and its basic parameters	Permanent electrode
	of element being determined	of internal standard		
Mg	Mg 5183·6	Cu 5153·2	Arc: $I = 2$–4 A	Copper
Mg	Mg 5183·6	Fe 5202·3	Arc: $I = 2$–4 A	Iron
Fe	Fe 5269·5	Cu 5292·5	Arc: $I = 2$–4 A	Copper
Mn	Mn 4823·5	Fe 4859·7	Arc: $I = 2$–4 A	Iron
Si	Si 6371·1	Fe 6400·0	High-voltage spark:	Iron
			$C = 0{\cdot}01\ \mu F$; $L = 0{\cdot}01$ mH;	
Cu	Cu 5101·5	Fe 5110·4	$I = 3$ A (simple connexion)	
Cu	Cu 5292·5	Fe 5269·5	Arc: $I = 2$–4 A	Iron
Cr	Cr 5208·4	Fe 5227·2	Arc: $I = 2$–4 A	Iron
Na	Na 5890·0	Fe 5914·2	Arc: $I = 2$–4 A	Iron
Zn	Zn 4810·5	Fe 4859·7	Arc: $I = 2$–4 A	Iron

The spectrum of the burning material is observed in the eye-piece of the spectroscope and a note is made of the time at which the intensities of the selected line of the material and a weak line of the substitute electrode, are equal. The time is measured by a stopwatch, reading from the moment the arc (spark) is switched on. The time interval recorded will be longer, the higher the content of the element in the deposited vapours. The burning-out time of the transferred material is a measure of its concentration in the test-piece. Calibration graphs are drawn up on the basis of standard specimens of known composition, by plotting the concentration of the element in the alloy against the burning-out time of the element being determined. The graph thus obtained is used in subsequent work to determine the content of the element in question in the test-pieces. The position of the graph should be checked periodically (twice or three times a week).

With this method the analysis error is generally 5–10 per cent of the content of the element. The method and concrete analysis conditions are described in Refs. 87 and 88.

In order to transfer material, contact-spark transfer of the sample may be used. The essence of this method is that the test-piece and the substitute electrode are connected to different poles of a capacitor changed by d.c. When the substitute electrode comes in contact with the test-piece the capacitor discharges and material is transferred (p. 140). The material deposited on the substitute electrode, is burned in an arc or a spark.

Observation of the transferred material can be used in the qualitative analysis of complex alloys. When transferred material is being burned-out, the spectra will only contain the most sensitive lines of the element, which simplifies their identification.

Determination of the Thickness of Metallic Coatings

In determining the thickness of metallic coatings, use is made of the fact that the breakdown time of the coating depends on its thickness. To determine the thickness of coatings, low-power spark or arc discharges are mostly used. The permanent electrode is cone-shaped and its chemical composition differs qualitatively from that of the coating and the parent metal of the test-piece.

During sparking, the intensity of the line of the coating element falls, while that of the parent-metal elements rises. The lines of the element of the substitute electrode remain more or less constant. Thus various procedures can be used to estimate the coating thickness:

1. The line of the coating element can be compared with that of the parent-metal element.

2. The line of the coating element (or of the parent-metal element) can be compared with the line of the permanent-electrode material.

In the cases mentioned the time is measured, at which the intensities of the analysis lines selected become identical. Using coatings of known thickness, a calibration graph is drawn first, plotting the coating thickness in microns along the axis of the abscissae and the time in seconds along the axis of the ordinates. A separate graph is drawn for each type of coating. The determination error is 15–25 per cent of the coating thickness[89,90].

CHAPTER III

PHOTOGRAPHIC METHODS OF SPECTRAL ANALYSIS

1. Equipment for the Photographic Recording of Spectra

Various types of spectrographs are used in the photographic recording of spectra. The main difference between them and spectroscopes is that the eye-piece for visual observation of the spectra is replaced by a camera for photographing them. The other distinctive features of spectrographs have to do mainly with their design.

Photographic materials can also be used in the ultraviolet region of the spectrum. Spectrographs designed for photography in this region should be fitted with a quartz prism. Glass prisms are used in spectrographs designed for the visible region of the spectrum.

Both quartz and glass spectrographs are classified on the basis of their linear dispersion. By linear dispersion of a spectrograph is denoted the quantity $(\Delta n)/(\Delta\lambda)$, which indicates the distance taken up on the photographic plate by the unit wavelength interval (Δn is the length interval, $\Delta\lambda$ is the wavelength interval). The greater the distance taken up on the spectrogram by a 1-Å interval, the greater is the dispersion of the spectrograph.

In practice the reciprocal of this value, $(\Delta\lambda)/(\Delta n)$ is mostly used. This ratio indicates the wavelength interval (in Å) occupying 1 mm of the spectrogram. The smaller this ratio, the greater is the dispersion of the spectrograph and the easier it is to distinguish lines with similar wave lengths on the spectrogram.

The KSA-1 (KS-55) spectrograph with interchangeable prisms has a high dispersion. With a quartz prism its dispersion in the region of 3000 Å equals 4·6 Å/mm, in the region of 4000 Å it is 11·5 Å/mm. For operation in the visible region of the spectrum a glass prism is fitted. In this case the dispersion in the region of 4000 Å is 5·5 Å/mm. For green rays ($\lambda = 5000$ Å) the dispersion is 11·6 Å/mm, decreasing on going to the longwave region of the spectrum. The KSA-1 spectrograph is used mostly to analyse materials giving spectra rich in lines, and also in scientific investigations.

The ISP-51 spectrograph is designed for carrying out spectroscopic investigations and practical analysis in the visible part of the spectrum. Cameras with a small focal length ($F = 120$ or 270 mm) are supplied with the spectrograph. Because of the high transmission of the instrument, spectra of low luminosities can be obtained with these small cameras. But on operation with these cameras the dispersion of the instrument is low. Thus, in analysing materials giving multi-line spectra (ores, minerals, certain alloys) cameras UF-84 ($F = 800$ mm) and UF-85 ($F = 1300$ mm) are fitted.

The great majority of spectral analysis problems can be solved using medium-dispersion spectrographs. The ISP-28 (ISP-22) spectrograph belongs to this class of equipment. It is widely used in the analysis of alloys, metals, ores and minerals. The part of the spectrum suitable for analysis lies between 2000 and 4000 Å. This spectrograph has a low dispersion in the visible region. For example, with orange rays ($\lambda = 6000$ Å) the linear dispersion is 110 Å/mm, while at $\lambda = 2000$ Å it is 3·5 Å/mm, and at $\lambda = 3100$ Å it is 16 Å/mm.

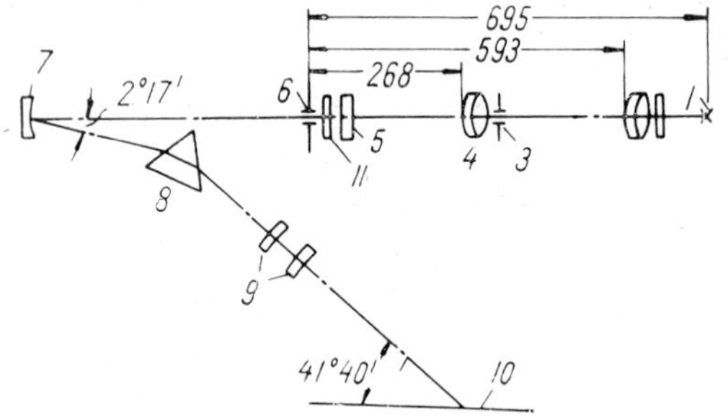

FIG. 48. Optical system of ISP-28 spectrograph.

1—light source; *2*, *4*, *5*—condenser lenses; *3*—iris diaphragm; *6*—spectral slit; *7*—collimator mirror objective; *8*—dispersing prism; *9*—camera objective; *10*—photographic plate; *11*—step absorber on diaphragm.

Figure 48 illustrates the optical design of the ISP-28 spectrograph with a standard three-lens illumination system. An image of the light source *1* is projected by the lens *2* on to an iris diaphragm *3* located near a second lens *4*. The condenser *5* fits against the slit of the spectrograph and provides more uniform illumination over the height of the slit. The spectral slit *6* transmits a very narrow pencil of rays that fills the collimeter objective *7*, which is a concave mirror 40 mm in diameter with a focal length of 703 mm. The parallel pencil of rays reflected from the mirror, falls on a triangular prism *8* and is dispersed into a spectrum. The spectrum is focused in the plane of a photographic film *10* by a camera objective *9*.

The whole of the optical system of the spectrograph, except for the illuminating lenses, is assembled by the manufacturer. The illuminating lenses are installed just before the spectrograph is going to be used.

Figure 49 shows an external view of the ISP-28 spectrograph. The mirror objective of the collimator, the prism and the camera objective are housed under a casing *1*. The width of the spectrograph slit varies between 0 and 0·4 mm as the cylinder rotates. The width of the slit is indicated on the scale of this cylinder to within an accuracy of 0·001 mm. In order to obtain a clear image of the spectrum on the photographic plate the slit can be moved along the optical axis by the drum *3*. The reading on this drum (the nul point of the slit) corresponding to a sharp image of the spectrum, is usually given

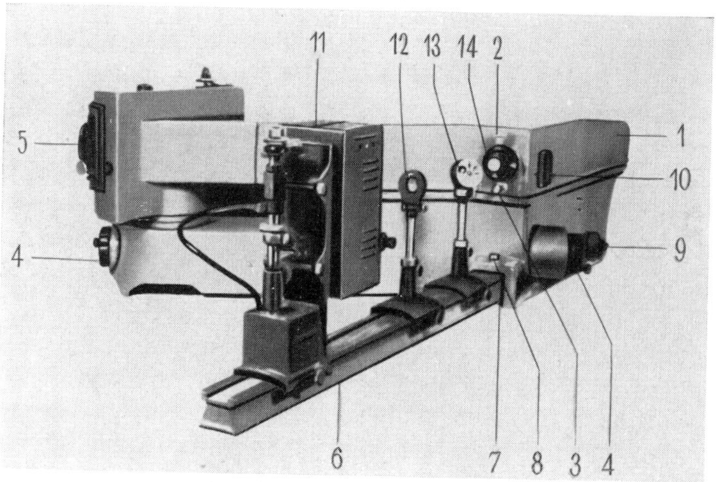

FIG. 49. External view of spectrograph.

1—casing; *2*—cylinder for setting spectral slit width; *3*—drum for moving slit along optical axis; *4*—knob for moving plate holder; *5*—plate holder; *6*—guide rails; *7*—cradle for fixing rails; *8* *9*—bolts for fixing rails; *10*—shutter; *11*—stand for fixing electrodes; *12*, *13*—illumination lenses; *14*—condenser cap for spectrograph slit.

on the rating plate of the instrument. The knob *4* moves the plate holder *5* that fits into the grooves in the plate-holder section.

The spectrograph stands on a table 80–90 cm high, allowing free access to the light source, the slit and the film holder.

The centre of the gap between the electrodes, and the centres of the lenses should lie along the optical axis of the collimator, i.e. along the straight line passing through the centre of the spectral slit and the centre of the collimator objective. The operation of coordinating the optical axis of the lenses and of the light source, with the optical axis of the collimator (adjustment), is based on the correct positioning of the guide rails. Adjustment is usually carried out twice.

The guide rails *6* (Fig. 49) fit into the cradle *7* and are fixed by bolts *8*, *9*. The free ends of the guide rails rest on a pin, by means of which they can be put in the horizontal position. A stand is fixed to the guide rails 15–20 cm from the slit, and a cap with a condenser $F = 275$ is placed over the slit.

After fitting the electrodes (it is better to use conical electrodes), the illumination lamp, mounted in a frame, is switched on. The electrodes are moved so that their image is symmetrical in relation to the cross-hair of the slit cover. In this way the electrodes can be coordinated with the optical axis. This coordination can be carried out more accurately by viewing the spectrum from the plate-holder side, and by setting the slit at the maximum width (0·04 mm) and restricting its height to 1 mm by the diaphragm. Then the arc or spark is struck and, placing the eye on the right-hand side of the opening in the plate-holder, the image of the electrodes is found in green light. This image should be in the centre of the camera objective, and to attain this position the electrodes should be moved to the left or right, and up or down. The image should not move when the stand is at different distances from the slit.

Once the electrodes have been correctly positioned, the first condenser ($F = 75$ mm) is adjusted. When ShT-9 or ShT-10 stands are used, the condenser is placed in the stand tube. To do this, the two set screws are loosened and the condenser is removed from the ring of a Reitor-type holder. After putting sealing rings on both sides of it, the condenser is fitted into the stand tube and held by a locking ring. The condenser is inserted in such a way that the flat cover-glass faces the light source. The assembled tube is inserted into the connecting piece fixed to the stand by means of a locking ring. By loosening this ring slightly, the tube is centered so that the image of the electrodes is arranged symmetrically in relation to the cross-hair of the slit cover. Then the source is moved to the required distance (Fig. 48) and a condenser with an iris diaphragm ($F = 150$ mm) is installed. The electrodes are projected sharply on to this diaphragm, and their image should be symmetrical in relation to the opening in it when it is in the centre of the lens. Where necessary, the condenser with the diaphragm can be moved up or down, and to the right or left, in order to give uniform illumination of the circle outlined on the slit cover.

Finally, the spectrograph can be adjusted by photographing the spectrum when the height of the slit is not restricted by the diapragm. The edges of the spectrum should be sharp, and the line darkening should be uniform over the height of the spectrum.

In setting the instrument, the position of the zero of the slit should be checked, by rotating the cylinder *2* (Fig. 49) anti-clockwise. The point at which the spectrum becomes visible from the plate-holder side should be noted, and the corresponding division should be used as the basis for recording the slit width.

The cleanness of the knife-edges forming the slit should be checked with the slit at a width of 0·005 mm, by microscope observation of the spectrum from the plate-holder side. The presence of horizontal bands crossing the spectrum, indicates that the knife-edges are soiled. To clean the slit it should be fully opened (0·4 mm) and the condenser cap removed, and the corner of a piece of clean tracing paper four sheets thick should be passed between the knife-edges. This operation should be repeated until the knife-edges are quite clean.

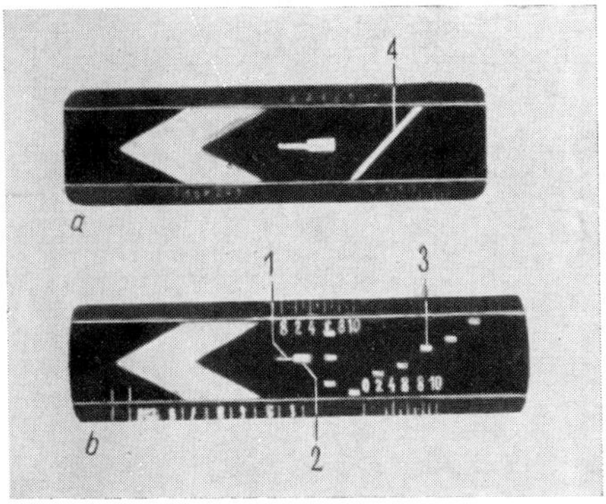

FIG. 50. Profiled diaphragms for restricting slit height — *(a)* with oblique opening for KSA-1 spectrograph; *(b)* stepped.

1—opening about 0·7 mm high; *2*—opening about 1·7 mm high; *3*—diaphragm steps; *4*—oblique opening 1·7 mm high.

The preparation of the instrument is concluded by checking the focusing of the spectrum. This is done by photographing eight to ten iron spectra with the micrometer screw located underneath the slit and intended for moving it along the optical axis, set at different divisions (width of divisions 0·5 mm). The slit should be 0·005 mm wide, and the exposure should be 10 sec (diapositive photographic plate, sensitivity 0·5-0·7 GOST units). The current intensity of the arc should be 5–6 A. The spectrum with the sharpest image of the lines should be selected, and the division of the drum corresponding to this spectrum should be used in the subsequent investigation (cf. Section 4, p84).

In photographing the spectra the height of the slit is restricted by the diaphragm. Figure 50 illustrates two types of diaphragms. If we place opening *1* against the slit, we get a spectrum 1 mm high (the magnification of the ISP-28 spectrograph is about 1·4). If we use opening *2*, we get a spectrum 2 mm high. To prevent the succeeding spectra from being superimposed on each other the plate holder should be moved this number of millimetres. This does not eliminate the likelihood of adjacent spectra becoming slightly displaced in the horizontal direction. Therefore spectra are often photographed with the plate-holder stationary, and different sections of the slit are opened one after the other by putting a multi-step diaphragm against it. In this way the spectra are not superimposed, only their edges come into contact with each other. When the plate-holder is stationary, seven spectra can be photographed with an oblique diaphragm opening, the second, fifth and eighth steps being used simultaneously. With these three steps it is possible to photograph three iron spectra, as required to carry out qualitative analyses. The height of the spectrum obtained with an ISP-28 (ISP-22) spectrograph is 2·5 mm with an oblique diaphragm and 2 mm with a stepped diaphragm.

2. Properties and Treatment of Photographic Materials

Wide use is made of photographic methods of recording the spectra in spectral analysis. In this case the light receiver is a photographic plate, which consists of photographic emulsion applied to a flat glass plate. The emulsion consists of crystals of silver bromide, containing a small amount of silver iodide, suspended in gelatin. The size of the "grains" of silver halide ranges between 5 μ and several tenths of a micron. Usually the grains have a diameter of about 1 μ.

Under the action of light chemical decomposition of the haloid silver in the grains begins, with the formation of atoms of metallic silver. As a result of this a latent image is produced. In order to obtain a visible image, it is necessary to treat the photograhic emulsion with a developer. Under the action of the chemical reagents contained in the developer, many milliards of molecules of haloid silver in the crystals that have absorbed light quanta undergo further decomposition. The haloid silver does not undergo decomposition in the grains that have not absorbed light. Thus, the visible image consists of atoms of metallic silver and is a negative; the lightest parts of the photographic plate appear as the darkest, and vice versa.

In order to remove the unreacted haloid silver from the photographic emulsion, the photographic plate is put in a fixing solution. Fixing dissolves the crystals of haloid silver and removes them from the photographic emulsion. The metallic silver is not dissolved. After being fixed, the photographic plate will not react to light.

The degree of blackening of the photographic plate depends on the intensity of the incident light I and the illumination time t. The quantity $H = k/t$, where k is a coefficient of proportionality, is known as the exposure. The curve correlating the blackening S with the logarithm of the exposure, is called the characteristic curve of the photographic plate. A typical characteristic curve is shown in Fig. 51, which shows that at very low exposures the photographic plate is insensitive to light. The minimum exposure at which blackening takes place, is called the sensitivity threshold (projection of section or curve from start to point A to axis log H).

A certain blackening of the photographic plate (fog) may be brought about by the developer which causes the haloid silver to decompose slightly. Thus the characteristic curve starts with a blackening greater than zero.

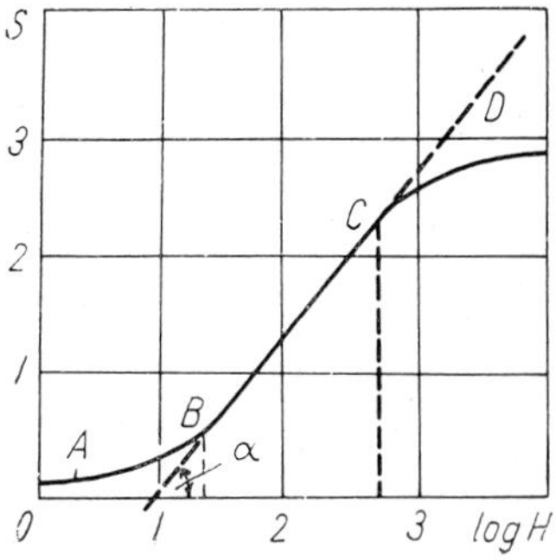

FIG. 51. Characteristic curve of photographic plate.

The characteristic curve can be split up into three parts. The centre part $B\ C$ gives the simplest, proportional relationship between S and log H: $S = \gamma \log H - i$. The factor γ, equal to the tangent of the angle of slope of the straight line ($\tan \alpha$) is known as the coefficient of contrast. The rectilinear part of the characteristic curve is called the normal exposure range. The projection of this range on to the axis log H characterizes the latitude of the emulsion, and indicates the interval within which the logarithm of the exposure is proportional to the blackening. The part of the curve $A\ B$ from the threshold of sensitivity to the rectilinear part, is known as the under-exposure range, the part $C\ D$ above the rectilinear part as the over-exposure range. Usually spectral analysis work is carried out in the normal exposure range. The normal exposure range is greater in the case of high-sensitivity plates* than in the case of low-sensitivity plates. The characteristic curve of a photographic plate can be plotted on the basis of a spectrum photographed through a nine-step absorber placed in front of the spectrograph slit.

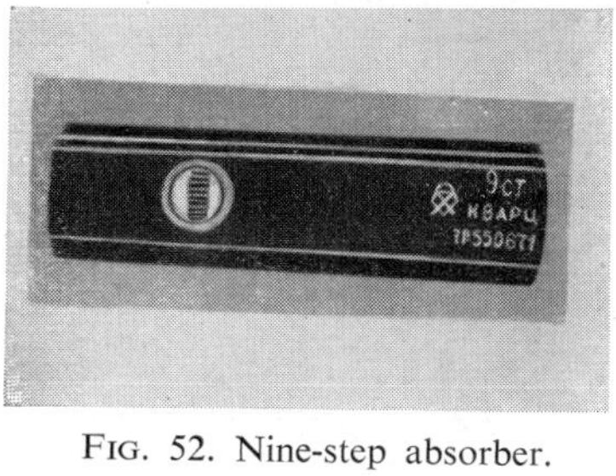

FIG. 52. Nine-step absorber.

* In the U.S.S.R. the sensitivity of photographic materials is determined on the basis of the system given in GOST 2817-45.

A stepped absorber is a quartz plate coated with uniform layers of platinum (Fig. 52). The thicker the platinum layer, the more strongly will the light be absorbed. The ratio between the intensity of the light that passes through a given stage, is called the transmission of the step. In relation to the transmission of the steps, various parts of the slit will be illuminated by light of different intensity. Thus each spectral line on the photographic film will be split up into sections of different degrees of blackening (cf. Fig. 65). The rating plate of the absorber gives the logarithms of the transmission of the stages, which differs from the logarithms of the intensity by a constant amount. Then the logarithms of the transmission (logarithms of the intensity) are plotted along the abscissae, and the corresponding blackening along the ordinates. The points obtained are then joined by a smooth curve (Fig. 53). The characteristic curve enables the intensity of spectral lines to be found from measurements of their blackening.

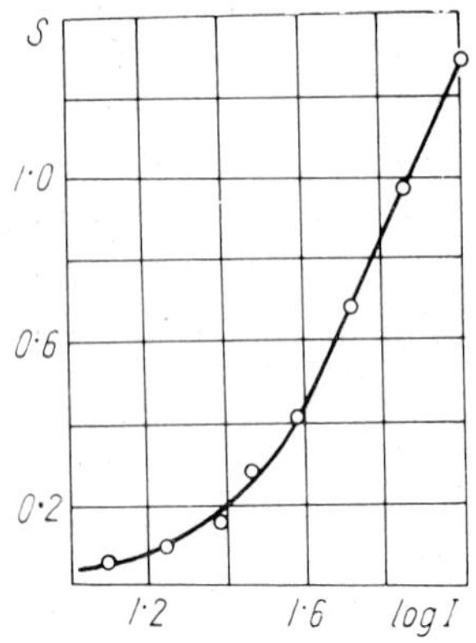

FIG. 53. Characteristic curve obtained with nine-step absorber.

Photographic plates react differently to light of different wavelengths, i.e. they have a varying spectral sensitivity. Emulsions containing haloid salts, react hardly at all to red, orange or yellow light and only slightly to green light. They are most reactive to violet light. In order to improve their sensitivity in the visible region, photographic plates are treated with various organic dyes, as a result of which sensitization it is possible to photograph spectra both in the visible and in the near infrared region of the spectrum (up to 12000 Å).

Photographic spectral analysis is carried out mainly in the ultraviolet region (2400–4000 Å). All types of photographic plates can be used in this wavelength range. Diapositive plates are most widely used. Our industry also produces the special high quality Type I, Type II and Type III "spectrographic" photographic plates, which are improved diapositive plates. Type II plates are more sensitive than Type I plates.[37]

The sensitivity of photographic plates diminishes sharply in the wavelength range 2400 Å and below, as a result of strong absorption of the short-wave radiation by the gelatin. The sensitivity of photographic plates in this region can be improved by treating them with a solution of sodium salicylate. In this way Type III plates are sensitive in the region of the spectrum 2400–1900 Å. Photographic plates where the emulsion does not contain gelatin, can also be used.

The coefficient of contrast of the photographic plate varies in relation to the wavelength of the incident light. It is greater in the visible range than in the ultraviolet range. Plates for spectral analysis have a more or less constant coefficient of contrast, 1 to 1·5, in the range 2500–3200 Å. This coefficient of photographic plates also depends on the developing conditions. It is lower in plates that have been developed at a low temperature or have not been long in the developer.

An important property of photographic plates is their resolving power. This is determined by the number of equidistant marks photographed per millimetre of the length of the photographic plate, that can be distinguished after suitable magnification. The resolving power depends on the grain size of the plate: it is higher in fine-grained contrasting plates, and lower in coarse-grained high-sensitivity plates. "Spectrographic" plates have a resolving power of 75–95 marks per mm. Even very narrow spectral lines in these photographs will merge if they are 0·01 mm or less from each other in the spectrograms. The resolving power of photographic plates depends on the developer, and is greater, the more rapid the developer.

Treatment of Photographic Plates

After being exposed, photographic plates are treated in a developer. Mostly standard developer is used, the composition of which is given in Table 29.

TABLE 29.

Reagent	Amount
Metol	1 g
Anhydrous or crystalline sulphite	26 g, 52 g
Hydroquinone	5 g
Anhydrous or crystalline soda	22 g or 54 g
Potassium bromide	1 g
Water	up to 1 l.

When the volume of work is small it is an advantage to prepare developer from two solutions. Such a developer can be stored for long periods. The two solutions are mixed together in equal amounts prior to being used. The composition of such a developer is given in Table 30.

Developer should be stored in the dark in sealed bottles with ground-glass stoppers. Developer becomes oxidized and loses its developing power when exposed to oxygen in the air. After use the developer should be poured into a bottle, which should be sealed tightly.

TABLE 30. COMPOSITION OF A TWO-SOLUTION DEVELOPER[3]

Solution A	Amount	Solution B	Amount
Metol	2·3 g	Anhydrous soda	46·5 g
Anhydrous sulphite	55 g	Potassium bromide	7 g
Hydroquinone	11·5 g	Water	up to 1 l.
Water	up to 1 l.		

In preparing developer the reagents are dissolved in distilled or boiled (40°C) water, in the order in which they are listed above.

Each reagent should be dissolved thoroughly before the next is added. The solution obtained must then be filtered.

Photographic plates are developed in red light (highly-sensitive plates in darkness), for the time stated on the packet of the developer. The developer should be at a temperature of $20° \pm 1°C$, and the prescribed developing conditions should be complied with as closely as possible. If the developing time is too short or the temperature too low, an under-exposed image will be obtained (gray and not black spectral lines will be produced on the spectrogram). Over-developing or excessive temperatures produce fog on the plate. Cold developer should be heated, and hot developer cooled. In order to develop more evenly the dish containing the developer can be rocked.

The development plate should be rinsed for several seconds in clean cold water, and then fixed. An acid fixing solution is often used, which rapidly halts the effect of the developer. In order to make the emulsion of the plate stronger, a hardener fixing solution can be used. The compositions of the fixing solutions are given in Table 31.

TABLE 31. COMPOSITIONS OF FIXING SOLUTIONS

Acid fixing	Amount	Hardener fixing	Amount
Hyposulphite	400 g	Hyposulphite	200 g
Anhydrous sulphite	25 g	Anhydrous sulphite	20 g
Acetic Acid (30%)	8 ml.	Acetic acid (30%)	50 ml.
Water	up to 1 l.	Potash alum	10 g
		Water	up to 1 l.

In order to prepare the fixing solution the reagents are dissolved in a small amount (less than 0·5 l.) of warm water, in the order in which they are listed above, allowing one reagent to dissolve completely before the next is added. After all the reagents have been dissolved, the solution is made up with water to 1 l.

Plates are fixed in either red light or darkness. To dissolve the silver bromide completely it is desirable to fix the plate until it becomes transparent, and then hold it in the solution for an equal period. At works, where it is unnecessary to keep plates longer than 3 months, the fixing time can be cut down to 5 min.

The fixed plate has to be dried. To accelerate drying, air is blown on to the plate from a fan above the bench. The plate is held vertical in a stand, and dries in 5–10 min. When the plates have been treated in hardener fixing solution, they can be dried in 2–3 min in a warm current of air. It is simplest to insert an electric plate between the fan and the plate support.

But it should be borne in mind that at high air temperatures photographic emulsion may melt. The plates should not become soiled with dust during drying.

The dried plates are marked for identification. The plate number, date and name of the operative who photographed the spectra should be written in ink in a clear area on the side with the emulsion on it.

Photographic plates require careful treatment. They should be held by the edges, and the emulsion side should not be touched with the fingers, otherwise irreparable damage may be done to the emulsion.

3. MF-2 MICROPHOTOMETER

The standard MF-2 microphotometer is used to measure the blackening of the spectral lines on photographic plates. The mechanism of the microphotometer is as follows. Light from a stable source passes through the photographic plate and impinges on a photo-electric cell connected to a sensitive galvanometer. The photo-electric cell will produce a greater or smaller photocurrent, depending on the blackening of the section of the plate being measured, and the galvanometer readings characterizing the degree of blackening will vary accordingly.

Figure 54 [(2)] gives a diagram of the microphotometer. The plate being studied is placed on the table *5*. The casing *2* contains a lamp *1*, light from which passes through a lens and objective system *4* and falls on the plate in a narrow pencil of rays. After passing through the plate and the objective *6*, the light falls on the mirror *7* and, after being reflected by this, passes on to a screen *8* with a slit in it and then on to a selenium photo-electric cell *9*. The current from the photo-electric cell is fed to the galvanometer coil and rotates it together with the mirror *10*. The intensity of the light falling on the photo-electric cell can be estimated on the basis of the angle of rotation of the mirror of the galvanometer. The rotation of the mirror is determined from the scale *12*, which is also illuminated by lamp *1* and is projected on to the screen *11*. Various sections of the scale are projected on to the screen, depending on the angle of rotation of the mirror, corresponding to the degrees of blackening on the parts of the plate being studied.

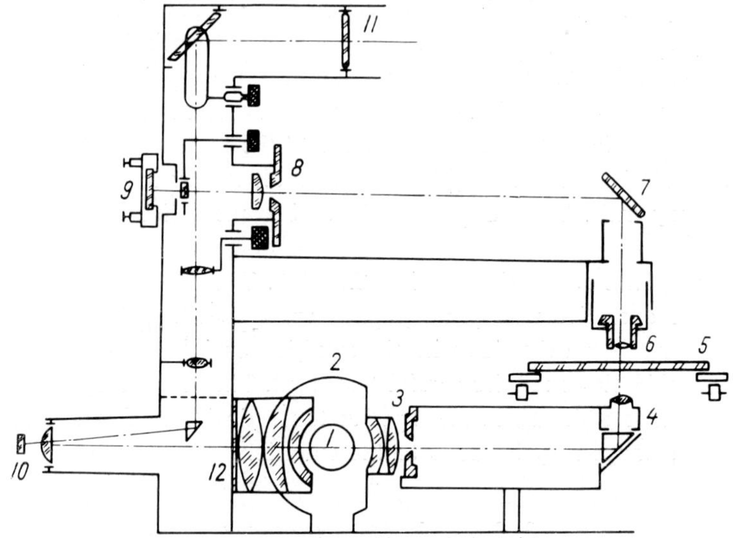

FIG. 54. Design of MF-2 microphotometer.

1—lamp ; *2*—casing; *3*—green light filters; *4*—lower objective; *5*—table; *6*—upper objective; *7*—mirror; *8*—screen; *9*—selenium photo-electric cell; *10*—galvanometer mirror; *11*—screen with image of scale of degree of blackening; *12*—scale.

An external view of the MF-2 microphotometer is shown in Fig. 55.

Before work is begun, the microphotometer should be carefully adjusted and set. The instrument, on a stand measuring 100×100 cm, fits on brackets mounted on a solid bench 60–70 cm high. The horizontal position of the microphotometer is checked on the basis of the level on the instrument.

After the microphotometer has been adjusted, the lighting of the screen *16* should be checked. The screen has to be illuminated fairly intensively and uniformly, and for this the lamp should be set correctly. The position of the lamp is controlled by screws in the cover of the lamp casing. If the lamp is set correctly, then when the lower objective is removed and a sheet of tracing paper is put in its place, a sharp image of the filament of the lamp should be obtained at the centre of the illuminated area. The lamp of the microphotometer (12 V, 30 W) is fed from an a.c. mains via a ferro-resonance voltage stabilizer and a solenoid.* The stabilizer ensures constancy of the light flux of the lamp, to within an accuracy of 0·2 per cent when the mains voltage fluctuates by up to 10 per cent. Since it is usually necessary to work from a 220 V a.c. mains and the stabilizer is built for 127 V, in addition a 220/127 V step-down transformer or a corresponding auto transformer with a

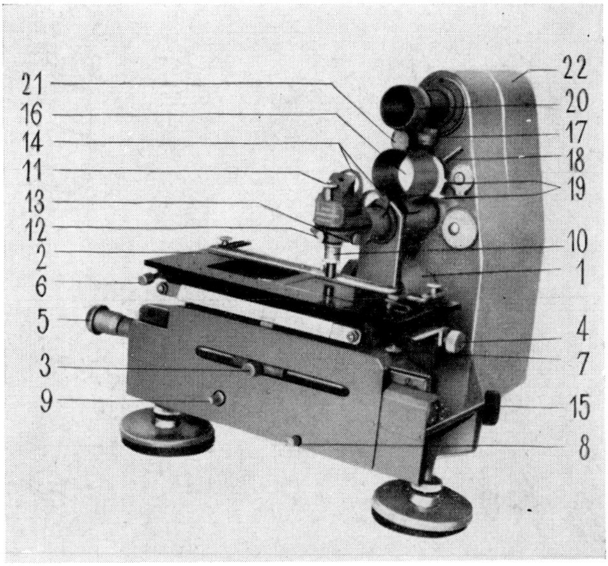

FIG. 55. External view of MF-2 microphotometer.

1—casing with lamp; *2*—microphotometer table; *3*—screw for preventing table from moving in longitudinal direction; *4*—screw for moving table in transverse direction; 5—micrometer screw for moving table; *6*—screw for turning table round longitudinal axis; *7*—screw for turning table in horizontal plane; *8*—neutral-key screw; *9*—button switch of photo-electric cell (in the latest models replaced by a tumbler switch); *10*—upper objective; *11*—screw for focusing upper objective; *12, 13*—screws for moving upper objective; *14*—lenses for further magnifying image of spectrum; *15*—drum for focusing image of green blinds; *16*—screen with image of spectrum; *17*—drum controlling microphotometer slit; *18*—handle for turning microphotometer slit; *19*—blinds restricting height of microphotometer slit; *20*—screen with image of scale of degree of blackening; *21*—drum for bringing scale of degree of blackening into field of vision of screen; *22*—protective casing of galvanometer.

capacity of 200–300 W, should also be used. It is possible, for instance, to use an ASS-0·3, ASB-03 or similar auto transformer.

After the lamp has been set, the protective casing *1* is opened and the galvanometer is loosened by turning the head *2* clockwise as far as it will go (Fig. 56).

---

* Until recently the lamp of the MF-2 microphotometer was fed from a battery.

In this way an image of the scale should be produced on the screen *20* (Fig. 55). The microphotometer has three scales. Mostly the centre scale is graduated in degrees of blackening, multiplied by 100. The scales are changed by turning the drum *21*. If a scale does not appear the galvanometer setting should be checked. After arresting the galvanometer, the horizontal position of its platform should be checked on the basis of the level incorporated in it. Where necessary, the fastening plates *5* should be unscrewed and the horizontal setting should be obtained by turning the feel *6* (Fig. 56). When the scale

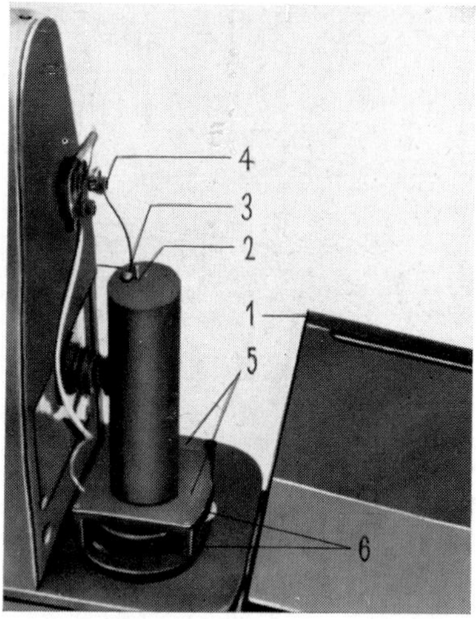

FIG. 56. Galvanometer of microphotometer.

1—protective casing; *2*—head; *3*—screw for turning image of scale; *4*—photo-electric cell; *5*—fastening plates; *6*—feet of galvanometer.

appears, its start (division ∞) should be made to coincide with the pointer on the screen. This is done by turning the knob up on the left near the microphotometer slit. If the start of the scale does not coincide with the pointer on the screen, then screw *3* (Fig. 56) should be turned carefully with the knob in the centre position. In this way the division ∞ is made to coincide roughly with the pointer on the screen. To improve the coincidence the knob should be used.

Then it is necessary to set the horizontal table of the microphotometer. The plate with the emulsion uppermost is fixed to the table *2* by means of a moving plate and spring-mounted grips (Fig. 55). The table is moved so that the beam of light passes through the far right-hand corner of the plate (the table with the plate is free to move 21 cm in the longitudinal direction and 8·5 cm in the transverse direction). By means of the screw *11* the upper objective of the microphotometer is moved to give a sharp image of the spectrum on the screen *16*. Then the table is moved in the transverse direction and by means of the screw *7* a sharp image of the spectrum is obtained in the near right-hand corner of the photographic plate. Then the table is moved back to its initial position and the spectrum is focused by the upper objective. This procedure is repeated until the spectra on the screen of the microphotometer become clearly focused when the table is moved in the transverse direction.

In order to focus the spectra in the longitudinal direction the table is set so that the beam of light passes through the far left-hand corner of the plate. A sharp image is obtained by turning the screw down on the left under the table. Then the table is moved and the spectra are focused in the far right-hand corner by means of the upper objective. This operation is repeated until the spectra are sharply focused on the screen.

By turning the screw *6* it is possible to ensure that when the table with the plate is moved to the right or left the image of the spectrum does not move off the screen or become displaced in the horizontal direction. The microphotometer slit is set parallel with the special lines by means of the knob *18*.

The image of the green blinds is focused on the screen *16* by means of the drum *15*. By turning the knob located to the right of the lamp casing, it is possible to bring the white band of light parallel with the lines in the spectrum. By turning the head by means of the same knob, the width of the band of light between the green blinds can be set at 2–3 mm.

The microphotometer slit should be in the centre of the band of light and parallel with its edges. This is done by turning the screw *13*.

The slit is set at the required width by rotating the drum *17*. The drum divisions each total 0·01 mm. It is best to make the slit width equal to two-thirds of the width of the spectral line on the screen. Usually the microphotometer slit width is made 20 times the width of the spectrograph slit. The reason for this is as follows. If the spectra were photographed at a slit width of 0·02 mm and the spectrograph magnification was 1·5 then, since the spectral line is the image of the slit, the line width on the photographic plate is 0·03 mm. Without the introduction of the supplementary lenses *14* the microphotometer gives a magnification of 20. The line width on the screen will thus be 0·6 mm, and two-thirds of this is 0·4 mm.

The slit height is made slightly less than the height of the spectral lines.

Before the measurements are begun, the beam of light is directed on to an unblackened part of the plate and the pointer on the screen of the blackening scale is made to coincide with the division ∞ when the photo-electric cell is disconnected, and with the division 0 when the photo-electric cell is connected.

When the division 0 is close to the pointer, it can be brought up to it by turning the screw *8*; this screw is connected to the neutral key, which can vary the light of the lamp smoothly between limits differing by a factor of 2·5 to 3.

It may be found that zero on the scale does not coincide with the pointer on the screen. If, when the neutral key is inserted, zero on the scale lies to the left of the pointer, then the stepped absorber can be inserted, which will reduce the light intensity by a factor of 2, 4 or 8. The knob of the absorber is located below the drum *21*. The final setting of zero is carried out by means of the neutral key.

If, when the neutral key is withdrawn, zero on the scale lies to the right of the pointer on the screen and the stepped absorber is not inserted, then the division coinciding with the pointer should be taken as zero. The number of the division corresponding to zero then has to be substracted from the measurement figure obtained for the blackening. When it is simply necessary to find the difference in the blackening of two lines, this correction can be dispensed with.

Before starting the measurements it is necessary to check the horizontal setting of the table holding the plate, the focusing of the spectrograms, the focusing and setting of the image of the green blinds on the screen, and the parallelism of the edges of the blinds, the mircophotometer slit and the spectral lines.

The lines being studied should be marked beforehand on the plates.

The table holding the plate should be arranged so that the line being measured lies near the microphotometer slit. The photoelectric cell should then be switched on and the spectral line should be brought up to the microphotometer slit by slowly turning the micrometer screw *5*. As the line moves across the slit, the readings of the blackening scale will rise at first to reach a maximum, and will then fall again. The maximum deflection of the blackening scale should be noted and recorded. For greater accuracy the recordings should be carried out two or three times. With a little practice good agreement can be obtained between the results.

4. QUALITATIVE SPECTROGRAPHIC ANALYSIS

By means of qualitative spectral analysis it is possible to determine the chemical elements present in a sample. This operation can be carried out by both visual and spectrographic analysis methods. The advantages of spectrographic analysis lie in the greater volume of data that is obtained, and in the greater possibility of checking and improving the accuracy. With visual analysis methods the spectrum is studied during arcing or sparking. With a spectrograph the processes of producing and studying the spectrum are separated from each other. This makes it possible to use instruments permitting accurate measurement of the wavelengths of the unknown lines, and also to reduce the likelihood of error in determining the composition of the sample. Moreover, spectrograms will cover a wide range of wavelengths, extending from the far ultraviolet to the visible and infrared ranges of the spectrum. The total qualitative composition of a sample can be determined on the basis of a single spectrogram.

In view of its obvious advantages, spectrographic qualitative analysis has been widely used in studying the composition of ores and minerals, metals and alloys, biological materials and chemicals, as an improvement on accurate chemical or spectral determinations.

Depending on the nature of the sample, various methods are used to introduce it into the discharge gap. Instudying metals and alloys, single-metal electrodes of various shapes are used. Powders and solutions are introduced into the discharge gap from the crater of a carbon electrode by compressed air, on special rotary electrodes and by other methods (cf. Chapter V).

The material of the permanent electrode (graphite, pure metals, etc.) should be free from the elements being determined.

Samples for analysis may contain various elements in concentrations ranging from 30–40 per cent to several thousandths of one per cent or less. When elements are present in large concentrations, most of their lines will be easily visible on the spectrogram. As the concentration of the element in the sample falls, the number of lines in the spectrum and their intensity will diminish. The most sensitive lines will be the last to disappear, and so these are called the "persistent" lines. These are generally resonance lines, that appear as a result of the transition of the atoms into the normal state from the first excited level.

Table 2 (see p. 25) gives the sensitive lines of the commonest elements.[14] Broadly speaking, these lie in the ultraviolet region of the spectrum. Against each line we give a rough estimate of the intensity during arc or spark excitation of the spectrum. It will be seen from Table 2 that most chemical elements have lines that can be excited satisfactorily in arc sources. In these sources intensive evaporation of matter takes place and conditions favour the excitation of the natural atoms, and also the ions of some elements. Spark discharge has to be used to excite the lines of haloids, phosphorus, carbon, sulphur and other poorly-excitable elements.

Spectra in the ultraviolet range can be photographed using quartz-prism spectrographs, in particular the ISP-28 (ISP-22) spectrograph. The dispersion of this instrument is such that the spectra of a large number of elements, including elements rich in lines can be analysed in the wavelength range 2000–3000 Å.

Iron, cobalt, manganese, vanadium, chromium, tungsten, molybdenum, titanium and other elements give spectra rich in lines. It is difficult to interpret the spectra of samples containing large concentrations of these elements. In such cases it is advisable to obtain spectrograms using instruments of high dispersion, e.g. the KSA-1 spectrograph with a quartz or glass prism, the ISP-51 spectrograph with long-focus cameras, etc.

"Spectrographic" Type II photographic plates (sensitivity 16–32 GOST units) are most suitable for qualitative analysis purposes. Type III plates are best for recording spectra in the 2000–2500 Å range. On carrying out analyses to determine the analysis pairs required for quantitative analysis, the plates recommended in the procedure should be used.

In cases where very low concentrations of impurities have to be determined, the presence of a continuous background in the spectrogram should be taken into account. This may arise as a result of light dispersion from the optical system, or because of broadening of individual spectral lines. In some cases the background consists of molecular spectra. In the case of arc discharge with carbon electrodes the spectrum of cyanogen (CN) is particularly intense—this covers the ranges 3500–3590, 3750–3885 and 4050–4215 Å. In work in the visible region of the spectrum, a very strong background may appear which is due to glow from the incandescent particles of the sample. A continuous background in also produced by other factors.(3)

The background of spectrograms can be greatly reduced by narrowing the slit width. Narrowing the slit width diminishes the background blackening more rapidly than the spectral line blackening. Usually slit widths of 0·005–0·01 mm are used in qualitative analysis.

The exposure time is selected on the basis of the sensitivity of the plates, the light source (and its conditions), the method used to introduce the material into the discharge, etc. On working with an a.c. arc ($I = 4$–5 A) the exposure time for metals and alloys is about 30–90 sec, in the case of the burning of powders and salts it is selected with regard to the total burning-up time of the batch being studied.

To determine the total burning-up time the spectra are photographed on a moving plate. To do this without interrupting arcing, the holder containing the plate is moved every 20–30 sec. In this way eight to twelve spectra of the sample being studied are photographed. On the spectrograms obtained, the line intensities of some elements fall rapidly while those of others remain constant or even rise. Thus, different elements enter the gas cloud at different rates. The burning-up time of the individual elements equals the total exposure time of all the spectra in which these elements appear. The burning-up time of the whole batch will be governed by the time during which the sensitive lines of the slowly-evaporating elements remain in the spectra, and may be very prolonged. In practice in such cases it is possible to restrict the investigation to the time in which the line intensity falls ten to twenty times (the blackening is reduced about to one-half to three-fifths) compared with the brightest spectrum.

The rate at which the chemical elements and their compounds enter the arc cloud, is also taken into account in carrying out qualitative analysis (see Table 47 on p. 149). The spectra of powder samples are photographed in steps. During the initial arcing period (60–90 sec), a spectrum is obtained that indicates the highly-volatile components of the sample (alkaline elements, alkaline-earth elements and others). Then, without switching off the arc, the diaphragm is moved in front of the spectrograph slit or the plate holder and the sample is burned at a higher arc current intensity. This spectrum indicates the poorly-volatile elements.

In order to interpret the spectra of the samples it is also necessary to photograph the iron spectra. To prevent the spectra from slipping relative to each other, instead of moving the plateholder each succeeding spectrum should be photographed by means of a stepped diaphragm or diaphragms with an oblique opening.

Equipment and Instruments for Studying Spectrograms

The iron spectrum photographed with the spectra of the samples being studied, considerably simplifies the work of qualitative anaysis. The wavelengths of the iron lines have been determined fairly accurately, and the wavelengths of the lines of the impurities in the sample, can be calculated on the basis of these. The wavelengths of iron lines are given in atlases of spectral lines. Such an atlas was given earlier for the visible region of the spectrum. Figure 57 gives a negative of the arc spectrum of iron the region 2354–3767 Å. The magnification of the atlas is 20, which is the same as that of the spectrum projector. Some special atlases[15–17] have the same magnification, but cover a wider range of wavelengths. They also give the spark spectra of iron.

The spectrum photograph for the atlas was obtained on an ISP-28 spectrograph with a three-lens lighting system. The spectrograph slit was 0·005 mm. The electrodes were pieces of U7 carbon steel. The spectrum was excited in an arc (DG-2 generator) at a current intensity of 3 A. The exposure time was 10–20 sec. The plates were Type III photographic plates (sensitivity 5·5 GOST units).

In addition to the atlases of iron spectra, laboratories should also have tables of spectral lines.(14) These should be consulted at all times, to determine the element to which a line of given wavelength belongs; they are also used to select analysis pairs, to decide whether lines can be superimposed on each other, etc.

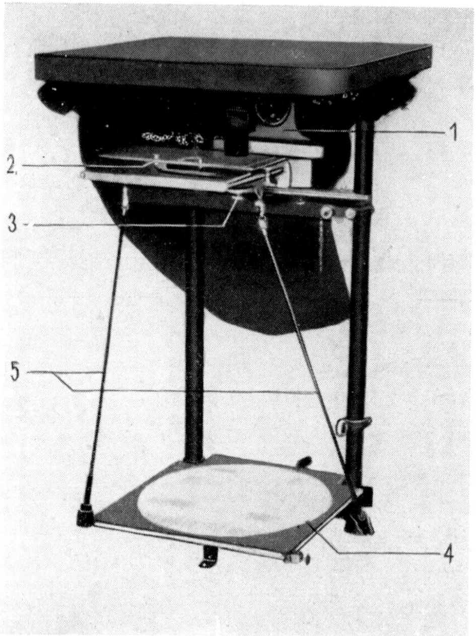

FIG. 58. General view of PS-18 spectrum projector.

1—head with turning prism directing light on to object table; *2*— for illumination lamp (not shown in fig.); *3*—objective; *4*—screen with image of spectrum; *5*—levers for moving object table.

The spectrograms are observed by means of spectrum projectors or the MIR-12 measuring microscope.

Figure 58 shows a general view of the PS-18 spectrum projector. Light from an incandescent lamp (100 W, 12 V) is passed via a right angled prism fixed in the head *1* on to the object table *2*. The spectrum is focused on the screen *4* by the objective *3*. The object table can be moved by the hand levers *5* in two mutually perpendicular directions, and the image of the required part of the spectrum can be brought on to the screen of the projector.

The PS-18 projector is delivered in separate units and should be assembled in accordance with the instruction sheet. After the framework, object table and projector have been assembled, the supply to the lamp is connected via a step-down transformer. The leads from the mains are connected to the inlets of the transformer, which are rated at 127 or 220 V.

After connecting the lamp, its adjustment should be checked. The circle of light on the screen should be intense and uniform. More accurate adjustment of the lamp can be carried out with the adjusting lens fitted to the projector. When the spectrogram is first placed on the object table (with the emulsion on the plate uppermost), a sharp image of the spectrum is obtained on the screen. Then the adjusting lens should be carefully inserted in the objective. Two images of the spiral filament of the lamp will then be visible on the screen. When the lamp is properly adjusted, the two images should be of

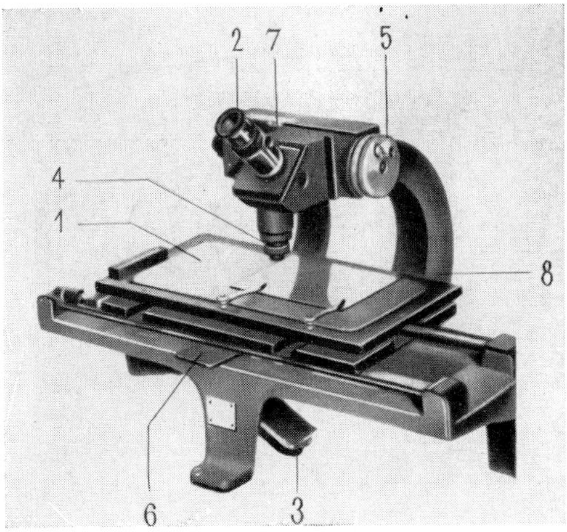

FIG. 59. MIR-12 measuring microscope.

1—object table; *2*—eye-piece; *3*—mirror for irradiating the plate; *4*—objective; *5*—drum for moving microscope; *6*—stop plate of object table; *7*—millimetre scale; *8*—plate.

uniform size and the spirals of one image should lie between those of the other image. If this is not the case, the spirals can be brought into the required position by turning the lamp round the vertical axis, and also by turning the three set screws and the nut controlling the height of the lampholder.

Spectrograms can also be observed by means of other types of spectrum projectors, e.g. the DCP-1 double spectrum projector.[(2)] With this instrument it is possible to project images of the spectra of two different plates on to the screen. One of these plates may contain the spectra of samples and standards, while the other may contain spectra of samples only.

The SPP-1 spectrum projector is now being mass produced. Here the object table slopes, making it easy to see on the spectrogram the lines required for analysis.

The MIP-12 microscope is used in making accurate measurements of the distances between lines. The photographic plate is placed on the object table *1* (Fig. 59). The optimum illumination of the visual field of the eye-piece is obtained by turning the mirror *3*. In the eye-piece *2* a small section of the spectrum can be seen. A clear image of the spectral lines is obtained by turning the objective *4*. Other parts of the spectrum can be obtained by turning the drum *5*, which moves the optical part of the microscope relative to the object table. Marks visible in the visual field of the eye-piece serve to indicate the position of the line. A clear image of these marks can be obtained by moving the eye-piece. The photograhic plates should be arranged so that the spectral lines remain parallel with the indicator as the microscope or the object table moves. The object table is moved by hand, by pressing on the setting plate *6*.

The position of the line is determined from the millimetre scale *7* and the drum *5*. The drum is graduated on 0·01-mm divisions.

Determining the Wavelengths of Spectral Lines

The wavelengths of spectral lines are determined by means of interpolation. We discussed this method in relation to visual analysis, where the distances between the lines were determined visually. If the spectrum is photographed on a photographic plate, the distance between the lines can be measured more accurately. This can be done by means of a spectrum projector, but mostly an MIR-12 microscope is used to measure the distances between lines.

Before measuring wavelengths of unknown lines a thorough study of the iron spectrum is required.

In comparing the spectrum of iron with its representation in the atlas, a start can be made with finding the following very characteristic line groups: 2395·4–2413·3, 2582·3–2600·2, 2950·2–2973·2, 3016·2–3021·1, 3067·2–3100·7, 3306·0–3384·0 Å.

In addition to these lines, other characteristic lines of iron can be noted and marked on the spectrogram. The wavelengths of the marked lines are determined by comparing the image of the spectrum on the screen of the spectrum projector, with the atlas. A spectrum with marked lines of iron can easily be interpreted.

After studying the iron spectrum it is necessary to determine the wavelengths of the lines in the spectra of the samples being studied. Let us consider the method of operation by means of an example.

Figure 60 gives a photograph of the picture observed in the field of vision of the eye-piece of an MIR-12 microscope. The iron spectrum I was photographed together with the spectrum of the sample II. The latter spectrum does not contain the iron lines but has a number of lines of other elements. We will determine the wavelength of line *1*. On each side of this line (not more than 5–10 Å from it) we will take two lines in the iron spectrum. In our case we can take the lines of wavelength $\lambda_1 = 3059{\cdot}1$ Å (*2*) and $\lambda_2 = 3067{\cdot}2$ Å (*3*). Putting the indicator mark on the first of these, we take the readings from the millimetre scale and the drum. Let us suppose that $n_1 = 39{\cdot}40$ mm.

Without moving the object table carrying the plate we bring the indicator up to the unknown line*. We get the reading $n_x = 39{\cdot}69$ mm. Similarly we get the reading for the line 3067·2 Å: $n_2 = 39{\cdot}925$ mm. The difference in the readings n_2—n_1 corresponds to the interval between the wavelengths $\lambda_2-\lambda_1$, the difference n_x-n_1 corresponds to $\lambda_x-\lambda_1$. Thus

$$\frac{\lambda_2-\lambda_1}{n_2-n_1} = \frac{\lambda_x-\lambda_1}{n_x-n_1}$$

From this we can easily express λ_x:

$$\lambda_x = \lambda_1 + \frac{\lambda_2-\lambda_1}{n_2-n_1}(n_x-n_1).$$

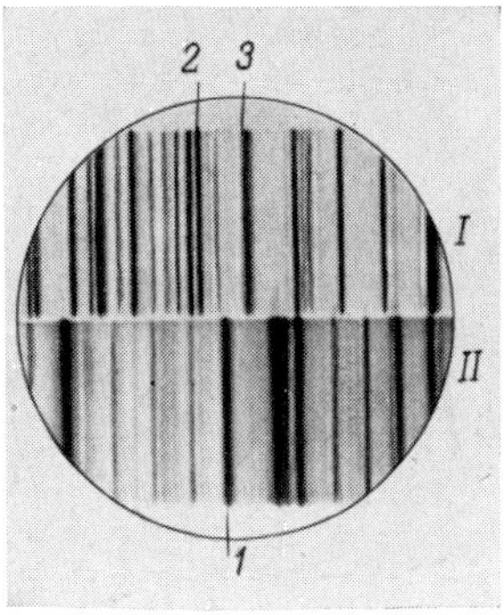

FIG. 60. Picture seen in field of vision of eye-piece of MIR-12 microscope (I – iron spectrum; II – spectrum of sample).

1 – line of unknown wavelength; *2*, *3* – lines of iron with wavelengths of 3059·1 and 3067·2 Å, respectively.

In the latter equation $(\lambda_2-\lambda_1)/(n_2-n_1)$ is proportional to the linear dispersion of the spectrograph in the wavelength interval being considered. The second term in the equation as a whole, shows the amount by which the wavelength of the unknown line exceeds that of the iron line $\lambda_1 = 3059{\cdot}1$ Å. Inserting the known quantities in the equation, we find that $\lambda_x = 3063{\cdot}6$ Å. The permissible measurement error in determining the distances between the lines was 0·01 mm. (The microscope measurement error is $\pm(0{\cdot}005+0{\cdot}01\,\Delta n)$ mm, where Δn is the measured distance between the lines. To reduce the error it is necessary to take the mean value of not less than ten measurements.)

In our case the error in determining the wavelength is about 0·1–0·2 Å. Hence, the wavelength of the unknown line is $3063{\cdot}6 \pm 0{\cdot}2$ Å. The spectral line tables contain an intense copper line, Cu 3063·4 Å, with this wavelength, and also weak lines of vanadium, titanium, tungsten and some other elements. The spectrum should contain other lines of these elements, at least more

* To avoid making mistakes in the readings due to the free motion of the micrometer screw of the drum, the indicator mark should always be brought up to the line being measured from the same side.

intense than the line we have found. We will take two or three of these lines for each element from the tables.[14] In particular, for copper we can take the lines Cu 3247·5 and Cu 3274·0 Å. Comparing the iron spectrum with the atlas, we find the required region, and in fact we find two intense copper lines of given wavelengths in the spectrum of the sample. Attempts to find intense lines of vanadium, titanium and tungsten in the spectra were unsuccessful. After this, there is no doubt that the line in question belongs to copper.

Such a check should be carried out every time, and attention should be paid to the lines of all the likely elements. First priority should go to the spectral lines of the widely-used elements. Rarely-encountered or poorly-excitable elements (the rare earths, inert gases, etc.) can be excluded from consideration from the start. The nature of the sample should be taken into

FIG. 61. Spectra of iron (*1*), type YalT steel (*2*) and nickel (*3*).

account. If a sample of commercial steel is being studied, then it is unthinkable to try to find lines of platinum, gold, germanium and similar elements in its spectrum.

The calculation of the wavelength of an unknown line and its identification with one of the lines given in the table—this then is the general procedure in qualitative analysis. In some cases the problem can be simplified slightly. Thus, an atlas can be used in which the position of the lines of the impurities is marked.[16, 17, 19] When working with a spectrum projector, such an atlas is laid on the corresponding part of the iron spectrum. Against the mark coinciding with the unknown line in the spectrum of the sample, the corresponding wavelength and the symbol of the chemical element can be read off. The presence of this element in the sample can be confirmed after others of its lines have been found. If the spectrum contains only the most sensitive lines of an element, then the results should be checked to see that the lines are not in fact produced through superimposition of the lines of other elements.

When it is necessary to determine the presence of given elements in a sample, then the most intense lines of these elements are selected from the spectral line tables and a search is made for them in the spectrum. Here it is advisable to select lines free from superimposition of the lines of other elements.

It is sometimes useful to adopt the method of eliminating the lines of individual elements. Figure 61 illustrates this. Here the spectra of pure iron, an iron-base alloy and nickel are compared. Most of the lines in the first two spectra coincide. They are emitted by iron atoms or ions. The other lines in the spectrum of the alloy belong to the alloying elements, above all chromium, manganese, nickel and the other elements most frequently present in iron-base alloys. The nickel lines can easily be identified by comparing the spectra of the alloy and of nickel. The number of lines is greatly reduced once the iron and nickel lines have been eliminated, and this simplifies the interpretation of the spectrum of the alloy.

5. PRINCIPLES OF QUANTITATIVE SPECTRAL ANALYSIS

Quantitative spectral analysis is based on the systematic relationship that exists between the intensity of the spectral lines and the concentration of the elements being determined. This relationship has been determined experimentally and can be expressed by the equation:

$$I = \alpha C^b \quad \text{or} \quad \log I = \log \alpha + b \log C,$$

where I is the spectral line intensity, C is the concentration of the element in the sample, and a and b are coefficients.[1, 2]

The line intensity depends on the quantity of material introduced into the discharge gap, the conditions of excitation of the spectral lines in the discharge cloud, and other factors.

It is impossible to achieve a strictly uniform introduction of the material into the discharge gap as well as constant conditions of excitation of the atoms. Thus, in practice, in spectral analysis the concentration of the element in the sample is determined on the basis of the intensities of two spectral lines. For this purpose, in addition to the line of the element being determined, a line is selected of another element present in known amounts in the sample (or else this element is introduced in known amounts into all the samples). Often the spectral lines of the base element are used in this way for comparison purposes. Thus, in analysing steels and cast irons an iron line is used as the standard line.

The lines selected should form a homologous pair. This means that their intensity ratio should be virtually independent of the conditions of excitation of the spectrum in the discharge. Moreover, the lines selected should be located close to each other and their intensities should not differ too greatly from each other. In the case of a homologous line pair the intensity ratio should vary mainly as a result of variation in the concentration of the elements in the sample. The lines selected for analysis are called analysis line pairs.

On the basis of the equation given above, we get the following relationship between the intensities of the lines of the element being determined and the standard element, and their concentration in the sample being analysed:

$$I_x = \alpha_x C_x^{b_x} \qquad I_0 = \alpha_0 C_0^{b_0}$$

The ratio of the spectral line intensities will equal:

$$\frac{I_x}{I_0} = \frac{a_x C_x^{b_x}}{\alpha_0 C_0^{b_0}}$$

where the subscript x refers to the line of the element being determined and the subscript 0 refers to the line of the standard element.

For analysis line pairs the coefficients b_x and b_0 are reckoned to be equal: $b_x b_0 b$, and the ratio $a_x/a_0 = A$ is constant for specimens of similar composition to each other. Thus,

$$\frac{I_x}{I_0} = A\left(\frac{C_x}{C_0}\right)^b$$

Expressing this logarithmically, we get:

$$\log\frac{I_x}{I_0} = \log A + b\log C_x - b\log C_0$$

This equation is used where the concentrations of the standard element in the specimens being analysed differ substantially from each other,

It is often necessary in practice to analyse specimens in which the concentration of the standard element varies only slightly. In this case the equation is simplified, as follows:

$$\frac{I_x}{I_0} = A_0 C_x^b \qquad \text{or} \qquad \log\frac{I_x}{I_0} = \log A_0 + b\log C_x,$$

where $A_0 = A(I/C_0)^b$ is a constant for the analysis specimens. According to the last equation, the logarithm of the ratio between the intensities of the lines of the analysis pair, is directly proportional to the logarithm of the concentration of the element being determined.

For analysis purposes standard specimens are required, with known concentrations of the elements being determined. The spectra of the standards and of the analysis groups are photographed under identical conditions. Knowing the concentration of the element being evaluated in the standards, and determining with respect to the standards the ratio of the intensities of the lines of the analysis pair, we can plot a calibration graph, where the logarithms of the concentrations are plotted along the abscissae and the logarithms of the intensity ratio are plotted along the ordinates. The plotted points can be joined by a straight line. By means of the calibration graph, the content of the element being determined can be found from the measured ratio of the intensities of the lines of the analysis pair for the analysis sample.

Three-standard Method

At least three standards are required in order to plot a calibration graph, because considerable errors may arise when two standards are used. The third point enables the straight line to be drawn more accurately and it is easier to estimate the accuracy of the measurement obtained for the standards and the analysis specimens.

The three-standard method is a fundamental and very simple quantitative spectral analysis method. Analysis by this method is carried out by photographing under identical conditions on one plate, the spectra both of the samples being studied and of three or more standard specimens. For greater accuracy the spectra of each standard and sample are photographed three times. The degree of blackening of the lines of the element being determined and of the standard element, is measured on the spectrograms.

The degrees of blackening are related to the intensities of the lines of the analysis pair in the normal exposure range, by the relations:

$$S_x = \gamma_x \log I_x - i_x \quad \text{and} \quad S_0 = \gamma_0 \log I_0 - i_0$$

or

$$\log I_x = \frac{S_x}{\gamma_x} + \frac{i_x}{\gamma_x} \quad \text{and} \quad \log I_0 = \frac{S_0}{\gamma_0} + \frac{i_0}{\gamma_0}$$

Usually, in the case of a homologous pair of lines located close to each other the properties of the photographic emulsion are preserved: $\gamma_x = \gamma_0 = \gamma$ and $i_x = i_0 = i$. Under these conditions we get:

$$\log I_x = \frac{S_x}{\gamma} + \frac{i}{\gamma} \quad \text{and} \quad \log I_0 = \frac{S_0}{\gamma} + \frac{i}{\gamma}$$

hence:

$$\log \frac{I_x}{I_0} = \frac{S_x - S_0}{\gamma} = \frac{\Delta S}{\gamma}$$

On the basis of the relation:

$$\log \frac{I_x}{I_0} = \log A_0 + b \log C_x$$

we get

$$\frac{\Delta S}{\gamma} = \log A_0 + b \log C_x$$

or

$$\Delta S = \gamma \log A_0 + \gamma\, b \log C_x$$

i.e. the difference between the blackening of the spectral lines of the element being determined and the standard element, is directly proportional to the logarithm of the concentration of the element being determined.

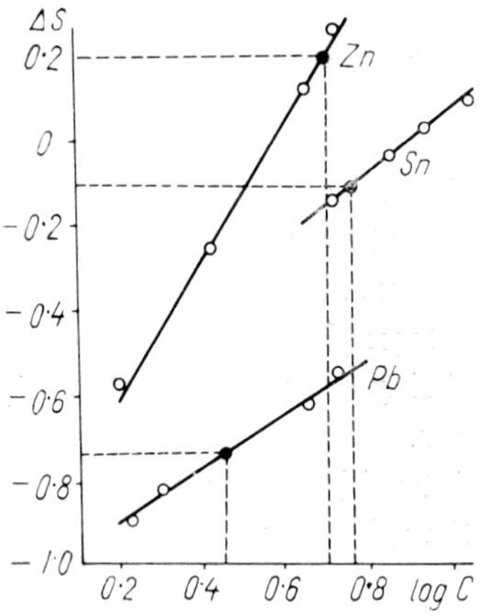

FIG. 62. Calibration graphs for determining tin, zinc and lead in tin bronzes, drawn by the three-standard method.

We can find the ΔS values for each spectrum on the basis of the measured blackenings. The values of ΔS_{mean} can be found from the three differences in blackening corresponding to each specimen. Then we plot the graph from the standards, and find the unknown contents of the element being determined, on the basis of the ΔS-values obtained. By analogy we can find the concentrations of the other elements present in the analysis specimens.

As an example we will take the case of the quantitative determination of zinc, tin and lead in tin bronzes (Fig. 62). Table 32 gives photometric data concerning the spectra, the ΔS- and ΔS_{mean}- values of the standards and the unknown specimen X, and also the logarithms of the zinc, tin and lead concentrations in the standard specimens of the bronzes.

In making the graphs the ΔS- and ΔS_{mean}- values should be plotted on millimetre paper using equal scales (usually scales of 10 or 20 mm per 0·1 of the ΔS-values or log C). Along the axes are plotted the ΔS- and log C values starting at their minimum values and ending with their maximum values. It is vital to locate zero at the origin of the coordinates.

With the three-standard method it is possible to analyse a large number of samples fairly rapidly. But it is not advisable to use the method to analyse one or two specimens, because much time has to be spent in photographing the standards.

TABLE 32. PHOTOMETRIC DATA OF SPECTROGRAMS OF TIN BRONZES

No. of specimen	Blackening of lines					Differences in blackening						Logarithms of concentrations		
	Zn	Cu	Sn	Pb	Cu	S	ΔS_{mean}	S_{Sn}	ΔS_{mean}	S_{Pb}	ΔS_{mean}	zinc	tin	lead
59	0·50	1·09	1·02	0·62	1·16	−0·59	−0·57	−0·14	−0·14	−0·54	−0·55	0·20	0·72	0·73
	0·43	0·98	1·14	0·73	1·29	−0·55		−0·15		−0·56				
	0·60	1·16	1·00	0·58	1·12	−0·56		−0·54		−0·54				
60	0·77	1·03	1·11	0·84	1·43	−0·26	−0·25	−0·04	−0·04	−0·59	−0·62	0·43	0·86	0·66
	0·85	1·10	1·32	0·76	1·36	−0·27		−0·04		−0·60				
	0·64	0·86	1·25	0·63	1·30	−0·22		−0·05		−0·67				
61	1·24	1·09	1·33	0·45	1·30	0·15	0·12	0·03	0·03	−0·85	−0·82	0·66	0·95	0·31
	1·05	0·95	1·42	0·56	1·36	0·10		0·06		−0·80				
	1·08	0·98	1·36	0·54	1·35	0·10		0·01		−0·81				
62	1·42	1·13	1·62	0·68	1·54	0·29	0·26	0·08	0·09	−0·86	−0·89	0·73	1·06	0·24
	1·59	1·33	1·54	0·55	1·45	0·26		0·09		−0·90				
	1·27	1·03	1·53	0·52	1·43	0·24		0·10		−0·91				
X	1·33	1·10	1·15	0·50	1·25	0·23	0·20	−0·10	−0·10	−0·75	−0·73			
	1·24	1·06	0·98	0·38	1·08	0·18		−0·10		−0·70				
	1·15	0·96	1·07	0·43	1·16	0·19		−0·09		−0·73				

Control-standard Method

With this method spectral analysis using only one standard can be carried out. Before carrying out the analysis an averaged calibration graph has to be drawn by the three-standard method.

The spectra of the standards are photographed to three to four times, using a three-stage reducer, on five to ten photographic plates of a single type, and supplied in the same batch with the same emulsion number. Here the analysis conditions, and especially the light source conditions, should be absolutely identical throughout. If plates of different types are used separate calibration graphs should be drawn. The developing conditions should be identical for all the plates.

In all the spectra the photometer measurements of the lines being determined are carried out without weakening, while those of the standard element are carried out with two steps, viz. a weakened and an unweakened step. The differences in the blackening ΔS are found for each analysis pair. In addition, the differences in the blackening of the weakened and unweakened steps, for the line of the standard element δS_0 are also determined.

A calibration graph is drawn on the basis of the averaged photometric data (ΔS) for all the photographic plates. This graph is used as the basis for carrying out the analysis. After the basic graph has been drawn, analysis can be carried out using one standard only.

While strictly observing the analysis conditions selected in drawing the main graph, the spectra of the analysis specimens and of one of the standards (usually one with a fairly average content of the elements being determined) are then photographed two to three times on the working plate. All the spectra are photographed with a three or a two-step absorber (for this, one of the outer steps can be stopped up in the three-step absorber).

The ΔS- and δS- values are found for all the spectrograms. The ratio $\delta S_0/\delta S = K$[39] is calculated from the basic graph and the working plate. To increase the accuracy in determining K, those steps of the absorber are selected where the line blackening lies within the normal exposure range and δS equals 0·3–0·5. By multiplying the differences in the blackening of each specimen by the conversion factor K, we get the new values $\Delta S' = K\Delta S$. To draw the working graph the point of the control standard $\Delta S_0'$ is plotted on the plane of the coordinates, and through it is drawn a straight line parallel with the basic calibration graph. Since the ΔS-values of the specimens are known, it is then possible to find the unknown concentrations of the elements being determined.

As an example, we will study the application of the control-standard method to the analysis of Silumins (silicon-aluminium alloys). For brevity we will simply consider the determination of silicon (the other elements are determined in a similar way).

Under selected analysis conditions the spectra of four standards of Silumins were each photographed four times on each of five "spectrographic" Type I photographic plates. A three-step absorber was used, the logarithms of the transmission of the steps of which were 0·85, 2·00 and 1·66, respectively. The analysis was carried out using the steps with a logarithm of the transmission of 2·00 (step I) and 1·66 (step II).

Photometer measurements were made of the line Si 2435·2 Å with stage I and Al 2652·5 Å with stages I and II ($S_{\mathrm{I\,Al}}$ and $S_{\mathrm{II\,Al}}$). We then found the quantities $\Delta S = S_{\mathrm{Si2435\cdot2\,Å}} - S_{\mathrm{Al2652\cdot5\,Å}}$ and $\delta S = S_{\mathrm{I\,Al}} - S_{\mathrm{II\,Al}}$, and also their mean values.

TABLE 33. PHOTOMETRIC DATA OF PLATE No. 1.

Standard No.	S_{Si}	S_{IAl}	S_{IIAl}	ΔS	δS	ΔS_{mean}	δS_{mean}
	0·52	1·02	0·69	−0·50	0·33		
1	0·61	1·13	0·79	−0·52	0·34	−0·53	
	0·47	1·01	0·68	−0·54	0·33		
	0·38	0·94	0·61	−0·56	0·33		
	1·05	1·28	0·95	−0·23	0·33		
2	1·12	1·36	1·03	−0·24	0·33	−0·24	
	1·03	1·25	0·92	−0·22	0·33		
	0·90	1·16	0·83	−0·26	0·33		0·33
	0·73	1·13	0·80	−0·40	0·33		
3	0·81	1·20	0·88	0·32	0·32	−0·41	
	0·68	1·10	0·77	−0·42	0·33		
	0·58	1·00	0·67	−0·42	0·33		
	0·95	1·24	0·92	−0·29	0·32		
4	0·98	1·31	0·98	−0·33	0·33	0·31	
	0·76	1·06	0·73	−0·30	0·33		
	0·95	1·28	0·94	−0·33	0·32		

Table 33 gives photometric data of the silicon and aluminium lines for plate No. 1. Table 34 gives the mean values of ΔS and δS for all five plates used in the analysis. Table 35 gives the results of the analysis. The δS_{mean} value of the working plate was 0·28, the δS_0-value found by averaging the figures

TABLE 34. MEAN VALUES OF QUANTITIES ΔS AND δS OF PHOTOGRAPHIC PLATES SELECTED FOR DRAWING BASIC GRAPH

No. of standard	log C_{Si}	No. of photographic plate										Mean values of 5 photographic plates	
		1		2		3		4		5			
		ΔS	δS	ΔS	δS	ΔS	δS	ΔS	δS	ΔS	δS	ΔS	δS
1	0·81	−0·53		−0·56		−0·55		−0·58		−0·54		−0·55	
2	1·11	−0·24		−0·30		−0·26		−0·27		−0·28		−0·27	
			0·33		0·29		0·33		0·35		0·29		0·32
3	0·93	−0·41		−0·46		−0·43		−0·46		−0·44		−0·44	
4	1·03	−0·31		−0·37		−0·33		−0·36		−0·35		−0·34	

TABLE 35. PHOTOMETRIC DATA OF WORKING PHOTOGRAPHIC PLATE

No. of test piece	S_{Si}	S_{IAl}	S_{IIAl}	ΔS	δS	ΔS_{mean}	δS_{mean}	K	$\Delta S'$
4 (standard)	0·95	1·23	0·95	−0·28	0·28				
	1·07	1·37	1·09	−0·30	0·28	−0·28			−0·32
	1·01	1·28	0·99	−0·27	0·29				
	0·87	1·21	0·93	−0·34	0·28				
8071	0·98	1·29	1·00	−0·31	0·29	−0·32			−0·37
	0·93	1·25	0·97	−0·32	0·28		0·28	1·14	
	1·02	1·23	0·95	−0·21	0·28				
8072	1·05	1·29	1·01	−0·24	0·28	−0·23			−0·26
	0·91	1·14	0·86	−0·23	0·28				
	0·94	1·28	0·99	−0·34	0·29				
8073	0·83	1·18	0·90	−0·35	0·28				
	0·86	1·22	0·94	−0·35	0·28	−0·35			−0·40

obtained with the five plates, was 0·32. The conversion factor $K = 0{\cdot}32/0{\cdot}28 = 1{\cdot}14$. We multiply the mean values of the difference in the blackening of the control standard (standard No. 4) by K. In this way we make the graph of the working plate slope parallel with the basic calibration graph. Drawing a straight line through the point corresponding to the control standard, we get the calibration graph for the working plate (Fig. 63).

By multiplying the differences in the blackening of the analysis specimens by the conversion factor, we get the new $\Delta S'$- values.

This operation can be carried out conveniently using a slide rule. The concentrations can also be found quickly by means of a slide rule when their logarithms are known. In our case the silicon concentrations in the analysis specimens are 9·9, 12·6 and 8·8 per cent.

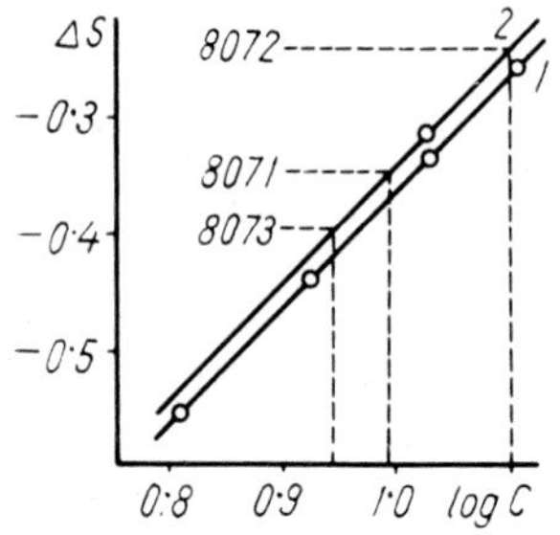

FIG. 63. Calibration graph for determining silicon in Silumin by control-standard method.
1—basic graph; 2—working graph.

To reduce the time spent on calculation a calculating machine of simple board type can be used,(3) or else tables can be drawn up and thus the need for calibration graphs can be done away with.

Instead of an absorber, homologous pairs of lines can be used of one of the elements where the degrees of blackening lie in the linear region of the characteristic curve and differ by 0·3–0·5, to find the δS-values. The lines selected should have identical excitation potentials in the region where the analysis line pair is located. The conversion factor K can be found from the ratio of the differences in the blackening of the selected lines in the basic and the working plates.

In the case of iron-base alloys the following arc lines of iron can be used: 2804·5, 2828·8, 2838·1, 2872·3, 2950·2 Å or 3153·2, 3160·7, 3200·5, 3205·4, 3222·1, 3225·8 Å.

In the case of aluminium-base alloys the arc lines of aluminium 3057·2 and 3050·1 Å or 2660·4 and 2652·5 Å can be compared.

Groups of homologous lines can be selected for the analysis of other alloys. Here it is unnecessary to select lines of the base elements. Thus, for alloys containing silicon the group of arc lines of silicon 2528·5, 2524·1, 2519·2, 2516·1, 2514·3, 2506·9 Å can be used.

It does not take long to go over from the three-standard method to the control-standard method. The ordinary analyses can be continued by the three-standard method, photographing their spectra with a step absorber. In making photometer measurements the blackening of the standard lines should be measured with and without weakening. When five to ten plates with spectrograms of the standards have been obtained, the calculations necessary for drawing the basic calibration graph should be carried out. In this way the two methods of carrying out quantitative analysis can be compared with each other.

With the control-standard method the analysis time is reduced because the spectra of only one standard are photographed. A considerable saving in standards is also achieved. The method is not inferior in accuracy to the three-standard method, and is often superior to it as a result in the decrease in the errors resulting from drawing the calibration graphs. The above-mentioned advantages of the control-standard method can only be obtained after long practice.

The Photometric Interpolation Method

The method of determining the ratio between the line intensities by means of visual estimation of the equality of their blackening, is widely used in practice in spectral analysis.(43)

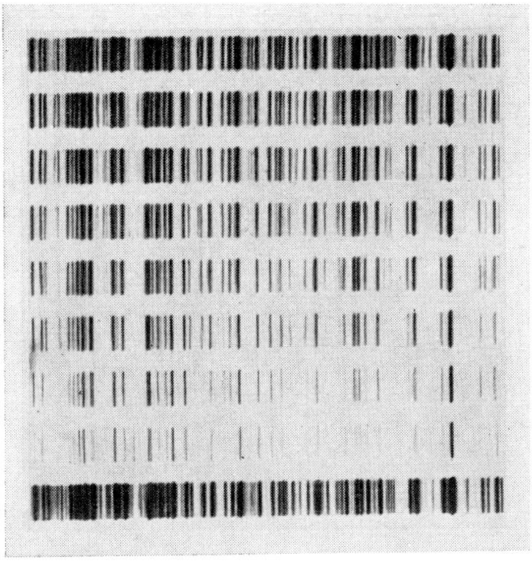

FIG. 64. Spectrum of iron obtained by means of nine-step absorber.

The spectra are photographed through a nine-step absorber placed in front of the spectrograph slit. Each spectrogram will consist of nine spectra of varying reductions in intensity (Fig. 64).

The relative intensity of two lines (the impurity and the base) is estimated as follows. The spectrogram is projected on to the screen of the spectrum projecter and a not very intense step of the impurity line, say step k, is selected.

In the case of the base line we find the step where the blackening equals that of the k-th step with respect to the impurity line, or else we select the two neighbouring steps of the standard line where the blackening is respectively greater and smaller than the blackening of the k-th step of the impurity line. Let us suppose these steps are l and $l+1$.

$$S_{l+1} > S_k > S_l.$$

We mentally divide the difference between the blackening of steps l and $l+1$ into n (usually 10) parts and determine the number of such parts which should be added to the blackening S_l (or subtracted from the blackening S_{l+1}) to give the blackening S_k. Let us suppose that we find that m parts have to be added to the blackening S_l. Then

$$S_k = S_l + \frac{m}{n}(S_{l+1} - S_l)$$

Let us consider a particular example. Let us suppose that the blackening of the third step of line Mn 2933 Å lies between the fourth and fifth steps of blackening line Fe 2936 Å. Then, dividing the difference in the blackening of these steps into ten parts, we find that three such parts have to be added to the blackening of the fourth steps of the iron line in order to attain equality of the blackening of the manganese and iron lines.

With the photometric interpolation method it is possible to use the logarithms of the transmission of the step absorber instead of the degrees of darkening.

When the logarithms of the transmission of the steps of the absorber are known, it is not difficult to find the difference between the logarithms of the intensities of the impurity and base lines. Let us suppose that the logarithms of the transmission of the third, fourth and fifth steps of the absorber (Table 36) are 1·05, 1·21 and 1·38, respectively. The logarithm of the transmission of the selected step of the manganese line is 1·05. In order to obtain the same intensity of the iron line the logarithm of the transmission of the absorber

TABLE 36. CALIBRATING THE ABSORBER

Step No.	Logarithm of transmission	Step No.	Logarithm of transmission
1	0·88	5	1·57
2	1·05	6	1·73
3	1·21	7	1·88
4	1·38	8	2·00

should equal:

$$1{\cdot}21+\frac{3}{10}(1{\cdot}38-1{\cdot}21) = 1{\cdot}26.$$

The logarithm of the intensity ratio of the lines of the analysis pair selected, can be found as the difference between the logarithms of the transmission:

$$1{\cdot}26-1{\cdot}05 = 0{\cdot}21.$$

In order to draw the calibration graph each spectrum of the standards is photographed with an absorber four to five times. The logarithms of the intensity ratios are found for each spectrum. The mean value of the logarithm of the intensity ratio is found for each element from all the logarithms obtained. Then a graph is drawn with the coordinates $\log (I_x/I_0)$, $\log C$. In order to carry out quantitative analyses of production specimens, it is now simply necessary to photograph the spectra of these specimens, but the graph should be checked periodically.

In order to speed up analysis, tables can be prepared before hand for the rapid determination of the logarithms of the intensity ratios of the analysis spectral lines. Eight values only need be selected for the line of the element beging determined (according to the number of steps of the absorber with varying transmission). In order to select a standard line of equal intensity, the intensity differences between the stages should each be divided into ten parts.

Taking the logarithm of the intensity of the standard line provisionally as 2·00, the logarithm of the intensity of the line of the element being determined can be found from the equation:

$$\log I = 2{\cdot}00+\log I_l-\log I_k+\frac{m}{10}(\log I_{l+1}-\log I_l)$$

Thus, to speed up analysis, all the possible values of $\log I$ can be calculated beforehand. Let us suppose that for the line of the element being determined we have taken the blackening of the first step of the absorber and we are going to compare it with the degrees of blackening of eight steps of the base line. Taking into account in addition the intermediate degrees of blackening, we get the table of logarithms of intensity shown in Table 37. This table is drawn up for the absorber, the logarithms of the transmission of the stages of which are given in Table 36.

The logarithms of the line intensities in Table 37 were calculated from the

TABLE 37. LOGARITHMS OF INTENSITIES FOR WORKING ACCORDING TO PHOTOMETRIC INTERPOLATION METHOD ($k = 1$)

Comparison step l	0.1 • m									
	0	0·1	0·2	0·3	0·4	0·5	0·6	0·7	0·8	0·9
1	2·00	2·02	2·03	2·05	2·07	2·08	2·10	2·12	2·14	2·15
2	2·17	2·19	2·20	2·22	2·23	2·25	2·27	2·28	2·30	2·31
3	2·33	2·35	2·36	2·38	2·40	2·41	2·43	2·45	2·47	2·48
4	2·50	2·52	2·54	2·56	2·58	2·59	2·61	2·63	2·65	2·67
5	2·69	2·71	2·72	2·74	2·75	2·77	2·79	2·80	2·82	2·83
6	2·85	2·87	2·88	2·89	2·91	2·93	2·94	2·95	2·97	2·99
7	3·00	3·01	3·02	3·04	3·05	3·06	3·07	3·08	3·10	3·11
8	3·12									

equation:

$$\log I = 2{\cdot}00 + \log I_l - 0{\cdot}88 + \frac{m}{10}(1{\cdot}05 - 0{\cdot}88)$$

$$= 2{\cdot}00 + \log I_l - 0{\cdot}88 + m \cdot 0{\cdot}14.$$

The tables for the other steps of the absorber can be calculated in the same way. In all we get eight tables. In order to find the logarithm of the intensity ratio of the analysis lines, 2·00 should be subtracted from the tabulated value of log I.

The ratio between the degrees of blackening of the lines of the analysis pair, can be estimated more accurately in the case of broader lines. Thus, for the purposes of photometric interpolation it is better to use wide spectrograph slits. The accuracy of determination is also improved if a step of the impurity line with not too high a blackening density is selected for comparison.

The determination accuracy of the photometric interpolation method is only slightly inferior to that of objective photometric methods, when the analysis is carried out accurately by experienced personnel.

Allowing for Change in the Concentration of the Standard Element

It often happens, in analysing specimens containing large amounts of the elements to be determined, that the concentration of the standard element does not remain constant (e.g. in analysing chrome–nickel steels, Fig. 71, p. 133). In such cases it is necessary to draw graphs in the coordinates ΔS and log (C_x/C_0) (or log (I_x/I_0) and log (C_x/C_0), because a rectilinear graph may not be obtained within the coordinates ΔS and log C.[40, 41]

From the proposed calibration curves it is only possible to find the ratio of the concentrations C_x/C_0. To find the concentrations as percentages, some simple calculations have to be made.

Let us suppose that a specimen contains three elements being determined, in concentrations C_1, C_2, C_3, and the standard element in the concentration C_0. In addition, the specimen may contain certain impurities which do not have to be determined. Let us assume that the quantity of these latter impurities is known, and let us denote it by C_{imp}. The total concentration of all the components will be 100 per cent.

$$100\% = C_1 + C_2 + C_3 + C_0 + C_{imp}$$

or:

$$100\% - C_{imp} = C_1 + C_2 + C_3.$$

Dividing the equation by C_0, we get:

$$\frac{100-C_{\text{imp}}}{C_0} = \frac{C_1}{C_0}+\frac{C_2}{C_0}+\frac{C_3}{C_0}+1 \quad (1)$$

From the calibration curves of the analysis specimen we can find the logarithms of the ratios of the concentrations and, by means of a slide rule, the ratios of the concentrations:

$$\frac{C_1}{C_0} = \alpha_1, \ \frac{C_2}{C_0} = \alpha_2, \ \frac{C_3}{C_0} = \alpha_3 \quad (2)$$

By means of this relation and equation (1), we can find the concentration of the standard element in the analysis test-piece:

$$C_0 = \frac{100\%-C_{\text{imp}}}{\frac{C_1}{C_0}+\frac{C_2}{C_0}+\frac{C_3}{C_0}} = \frac{100\%-C_{\text{imp}}}{\alpha_1+\alpha_2+\alpha_3+1}$$

The concentrations of the elements being determined, can be found from equation (2):

$$C_1 = C_0\alpha_1, \qquad C_2 = C_0\alpha_2, \qquad C_3 = C_0\alpha_3.$$

Similar results can also be obtained, whatever the number of elements to be determined.

Allowing for the Background in Drawing Calibration Graphs

The presence of background near the analysis line pair leads to a decrease in the slope and distortion of the calibration graph. When the background is pronounced its intensity has to be allowed for.

To do this, with a nine-step absorber a photograph is taken of the spectrum of the test-pieces on a photographic plate, and characteristic curves are plotted for the spectral lines, on which background is superimposed. From these curves, on the basis of the blackening of the line and the background S_{l+b} and of the background S_b we can find the corresponding logarithms of the intensity $\log I_{l+b}$ and $\log I_b$. Usually we take the mean value of the blackening of the background, measured to right and left of the line. Then we determine the intensities I_{l+b}, I_b and $I_l = I_{l+b}-I_b$. Having found in this way the intensities of the lines of the element being determined and of the standard element, we can draw calibration graphs in the system of coordinates $\log (I_x/I_0)$ and $\log C$ (or $\log (I_x/I_0)$ and $\log (C_x/C_0)$.

An example will illustrate this. Background with a logarithm of intensity of 0·60, is superimposed on a line of the element to be determined and on a

TABLE 38. ALLOWING FOR BACKGROUND

No. of standard	log C	$\log I_{x_l+b}$	$\log I_{0_l+b}$	$\log \frac{I_{x_l+b}}{I_{0_l+b}}$	$\log I_b$	I_{x_l+b}	I_{0_l+b}	I_b	I_{x_l}	I_{0_l}	$\log I_{x_l}$	$\log I_{0_l}$	$\log \frac{I_{x_l}}{I_{0_l}}$
1	−2·80	0·76	0·98	−0·22	0·60	5·80	9·60	4·00	1·80	5·60	0·25	0·75	−0·50
2	−2·51	0·86	0·95	−0·09	0·60	7·20	9·00	4·00	3·20	5·00	0·50	0·70	−0·19
3	−2·19	0·95	0·90	0·05	0·60	9·00	8·00	4·00	5·00	4·00	0·70	0·60	0·09
4	−1·90	1·30	1·01	0·29	0·60	20·00	10·00	4·00	16·00	6·30	1·20	0·80	0·40

line of the standard element. The logarithms of the intensities of the analysis lines are given in Table 38. Figure 65 gives the calibration curves with and without allowance being made for the background.

If allowance has to be made for background very often during analysis work, tables should be drawn up to enable $\log I_l$ to be found on the basis of the values $\log I_{l+b}$ and $\log I_b$. Such tables are given in Refs. 3 and 9.

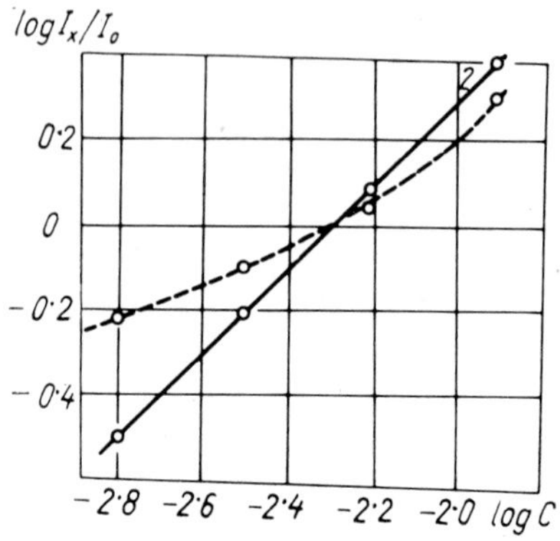

FIG. 65. Calibration graph without (*1*) and with (*2*) allowance for background.

When allowance is made for the background, it is possible to determine small concentrations of elements quantitatively when the spectral lines do not stand out very clearly against the general background.(42) With this method it is also possible to take into account the superimposition of the spectral lines of other elements on the lines of the elements being determined.

Sometimes the background is used as a standard for comparison with the compound being determined. In this case the calibration graph should be drawn within the system of coordinates $\log (I_x/I_0)$ and $\log C$.

CHAPTER IV

PROCEDURES FOR THE SPECTROGRAPHIC QUANTITATIVE ANALYSIS OF METALS AND ALLOYS

1. Development of Procedures for Quantitative Spectral Analysis

Numerous procedures are given in the literature for the quantitative spectral analysis of various materials—metals, alloys, solutions, and powders. Few of these procedures can be used directly and they have to be adapted on the basis of practical tests for specific laboratory conditions. This is the case also with the methods that are based on the use of standard apparatus. The fact that it is impossible to reproduce the analysis conditions very accurately, is a complication in the development of standard methods. Recently in fact, projects have appeared for methods of analysing certain alloys.

We will now study in detail the problems connected with the development of spectral analysis. In developing new methods attention has to be paid to the selection of the standard specimens and the analysis conditions, and to the estimation of the accuracy of the analysis.

Selection of Standards

Standards for quantitative spectral analysis should resemble the analysis specimens as closely as possible, i.e. they should correspond to them in chemical composition, structure, mass and shape.(7)

One of the most difficult problems is the preparation of the standards. Standards of a few alloys only are available from central suppliers. Standards for the study of current-conducting materials are hardly available at all. Thus, workers at spectral analysis laboratories often have to make their own standards.

It is simplest to use the test-pieces produced for routine analysis in chemical laboratories. The test-pieces selected should be analysed not less than five times and as carefully as possible, and then the mean concentrations should be determined. It is advisable to analyse these specimens in a number of leading laboratories.

A check should be made as to the uniformity of the chemical composition of the standard specimens. For this purpose samples for analysis should be taken from various parts of a single specimen. In the case of powder samples, uniformity can be achieved by thoroughly mixing the standard specimens selected. Solutions are the most uniform standards.

The elements being determined in the standards should be present in the form of the same chemical compounds as in the analysis specimens. Otherwise the results of spectral analysis may differ appreciably from those of the chemical analysis.

The presence in the sample of other impurities in addition to the element being determined and the internal standard, may also affect the results of spectral analysis. The effect of additional impurities (the so-called "third bodies") is noteworthy in the analysis of a large number of materials, in particular copper-base alloys.

Considerable errors may arise if the analysis specimens differ a great deal from the standards in their structure, mass and shape. Specimens of small mass cannot be analysed by means of standards of large mass, and vice versa.

The standards and analysis specimens should be prepared for analysis using the same procedure. For instance, it is impossible to analyses specimens of metals that have been ground flat, using standards that have been ground conical. The analysis specimens and the standards for quantitative spectral analysis, and also the permanent electrodes, should generally be ground on a lathe. Manual grinding is permissible in the case of flat grinding only.

In the standards the concentrations of the elements being determined should extend beyond the limiting concentrations of these elements in the analysis specimens. The standards should also include one having a chemical composition very close to the mean composition of the analysis samples. The concentrations of the elements being determined in the standards should be selected in such a way that the position of the points obtained from the standards lie as equidistantly as possible along the axis corresponding to the logarithm of the concentration. To find these positions the difference between the logarithms of the concentrations of the outermost standards should be divided by a figure equal to one less than the number of standards i.e. by the number of parts into which the concentration axis is divided:

$$\Delta \log C = \frac{\log C_{max} - \log C_{min}}{n-1}$$

where $\log C_{max}$ is the logarithm of the maximum concentration of the element, $\log C_{min}$ is the logarithm of the minimum concentration of the element, and n is the number of standards. Let us suppose, for instance, that the nickel concentration in the standard specimens of steels ranges between 2 and

16 per cent and that four standards have to be prepared. The logarithms of the outermost standards and the difference between them are:

$$\log C_{max} = \log 16 = 1{\cdot}20; \quad \log C_{min} = \log 2 = 0{\cdot}30; \quad \log 16 - \log 2 = 0{\cdot}90$$

This section of the axis of the logarithms of the concentrations must be divided into three equal parts. In our case $\log C = 0{\cdot}90/3 = 0{\cdot}30$, and hence the various logarithms of the concentration, will each differ from each other by 0·30, viz. 0·3, 0·6, 0·9, 1·2; the corresponding concentrations will therefore be 2, 4, 8, 16 per cent. The concentrations of the other elements being determined should be selected in a similar way.

The sum of the concentrations of the various elements being determined, should be about the same in all the standards. Thus, for instance, let us suppose that in order to study tin bronzes the standards have to contain 4, 6, 8 and 12 per cent of tin, 2, 3, 5 and 8 per cent of zinc and 2, 3, 5 and 8 per cent of lead. Table 39 gives one of the most suitable assortments of concentrations for these standards.

TABLE 39. CONCENTRATIONS OF ELEMENTS BEING EVALUATED IN STANDARDS OF TIN BRONZES (%)

No. of standard	Tin	Zinc	Lead	Sum of concentrations
1	8	6	2	16
2	5	4	8	17
3	3	8	5	16
4	4	12	3	17

Standards having the required concentrations can easily be prepared for powders and solutions. It is more difficult to make metal standards, because to melt these, careful calculation of the charge composition is required. The losses of the individual components of the melt through burning, are governed by the temperature conditions in the furnace, and cannot always be predicted. Thus, after melting, the composition of the specimen will differ to a greater or lesser extent from the prescribed composition. The metal should be stirred carefully during melting. The high frequency induction furnace is most suitable for making metal standards. The standards should undergo careful chemical analysis after melting, and the correspondence between their structure and that of samples melted at the works should be checked.

We will now study the problems of preparing the specimens for analysis and of selecting the optimum light source regime and the condition for photographing the spectra.

Preparation of Specimens for Analysis

In preparing specimens for analysis, the permanent electrode material, the shape of the electrodes and the length of the gap between them, should be selected with care.

In the spectral analysis of certain materials, where possible efforts should be made to use two electrodes of the same material. But such paired electrodes cannot always be produced. Moreover, the analysis specimens may differ from each other in their shapes and dimensions. Thus it is not always advisable to cut two identical electrodes from specimens, instead it may be preferable to use a substitute electrode made of material different from that being analysed.

The permanent electrodes are usually made from neutral material not containing the elements being determined in the sample. The spectrum of the permanent electrode should not be rich in lines and its lines should not interfere with those of the elements being determined.

Quantitative spectral analysis of metals and alloys is carried out with "neutral" permanent electrodes or with electrodes made of pure metal identical with the base metal of the alloy.

Steels and cast iron are usually analysed using copper or carbon permanent electrodes. A magnesium permanent electrode can be used in the spectral determination of carbon in steel. Steels are sometimes analysed using a permanent electrode of commercial pure iron (electrodes of Armco iron or of carbon steel are also used).

The analysis of aluminium alloys is carried out with paired electrodes of identical composition, or with permanent electrodes of pure aluminium. Carbon permanent electrodes can also be used.

Copper-base alloys can best be analysed using carbon permanent electrodes. Nickel electrodes can be used when determination of nickel is not required. When "third-body" elements are not present, copper permanent electrodes can be used.

Carbon makes good permanent electrodes. The spectrum of carbon does not contain many lines, and it is only in the region above 3400 Å that bright cyanogen bands appear. Carbon is easily machinable, and can be shaped as desired.

Carbon electrodes can be ground rapidly by means of a small electric motor of the type used in sewing machines. A chuck should be mounted on the shaft of the motor, into which a bit or cutting tools can be fitted (Fig. 66). Depending on the type of cutter used, the electrodes produced may be conical, hemispherical, cylindrical with hollows of different depth and diameter, etc. The cutters can be made from hacksaw blades.

The permanent electrode should be shaped in such a way that it does not burn away much during analysis, and that after analysis the shape of the electrode and the length of the gap between the electrodes are more or less the same as at the start of the analysis. In addition, the discharge should not stray unduly over the surface of the analysis specimen. The scatter of the discharge in relation to the optical axis should not exceed 1–1·5 mm.

Permanent electrodes are usually wedge-shaped or hemispherical. The analysis specimens are usually ground flat.

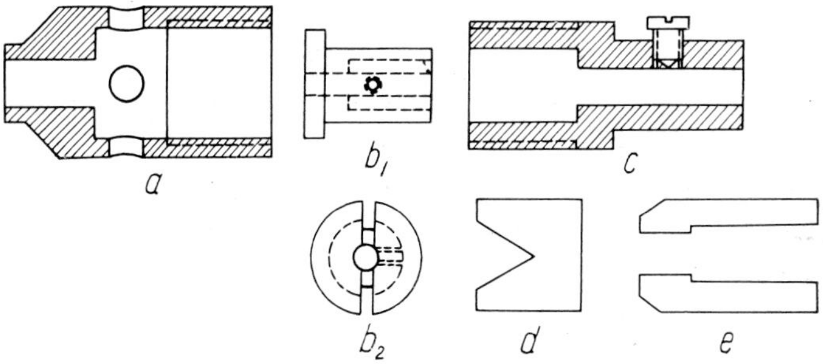

FIG. 66. Chuck for grinding carbon electrodes.
a—head; b_1, b_2—cutter and drill holder in two projections; *c*—chuck bed; *d*, *e*—cutters.

The length of the analysis gap normally ranges between 1·5 and 3 mm. If it varies, the conditions of excitation of the spectrum may also vary. To improve the condition of excitation of spark lines in particular, the gap should be shortened.

The Conditions for Photographing the Spectra

The results obtained when photographing the spectra depend on the width of the spectrograph slit, the method used to illuminate it, the sensitivity of the photographic plates, and the exposure. The width of the spectrograph slit is selected on the basis of the number of lines contained in the spectrum of the analysis specimen.

Usually the slit-width of the ISP-28 spectrograph is set at 0·03 mm when working with alloys not containing many lines (e.g. copper- and aluminium-base alloys), and at 0·01 mm when working with high-alloy steels.

As the slit-width diminishes the intensity of the background decreases more rapidly than the intensity of the spectral lines. Therefore in qualitative analysis, when fine details of the spectrum are to be distinguished, a slit-width of 0·005 mm is sometimes used.

To illuminate the slit with light from an arc or a spark, a three-lens lighting system is normally used, which provides uniform and fairly intensive light distribution over the whole height of the spectrograph slit.

It is sometimes desired to obtain more intensive illumination of the slit than that provided by the three-lens system. For this purpose it is possible by means of a single lens to concentrate a slightly diffused image of the light source on the spectrograph slit. It is also possible to set the light source 10–15 cm from the spectrograph slit. In these ways the intensity of the spectrum can be increased several fold without greatly diminishing its quality, but this does not noticeably affect the results of spectral analysis by photographic methods.

Low-sensitivity high-contrast photographic plates are usually used in quantitative spectral analysis, because it is assumed that the intensity of the spectrum of the analysis specimen remains constant throughout the exposure time. But in burning small quantities of material sensitive plates have to be used. Sensitive plates should also be used to determine low contents of phosphorus, carbon, sulphur and other elements in metals, that burn up rapidly at the start of exposure. The spectral line intensity of these elements diminishes rapidly during exposure. When low-sensitivity plates are used the spectral lines of these elements, when they are present in small concentrations in the sample, may be very weak, or may not appear, even at very long exposures. The lines of these elements may on the other hand be seen quite clearly at short exposures, on high-sensitivity plates.

Selection of Light Source Regime

The success of quantitative spectral analysis depends largely on the selection of the light source. The preliminary heating time and the exposure time depend on the electrical regime of the source. By rational selection of the light source regime it is possible to reduce the effects of various factors on the analysis results and thus improve the accuracy of the determinations.

In developing procedures for quantitative spectral analysis it is advisable to photograph the spectra through a nine-step absorber. The spectra of two specimens containing widely differing concentrations of the elements being determined should be photographed under three to four light source regimes, two to three times under each regime, at exposures of 1–3 min. The electrical regimes of the light source should be fairly diverse. Thus, in a d.c. arc a specimen can be photographed at currents of 2, 4 and 8 A with exposures of 1–2 min. In a high-voltage spark, spectra can be photographed with an inductance of 0·05 mH and capacitances of 0·005, 0·01 and 0·02 μF. The current intensity in the spark should be such as to produce a single spark discharge every half cycle of the a.c. Where necessary the current can be lowered or raised. Usually, with a capacitance of 0·005 μF a current intensity of about 1 A will suffice to produce a discharge every half-period of the d.c. with 0·01 μF about 1·5 A, and with 0·02 μF about 3 A will be required. The exposure time in the spark is 2–3 min on photographing with a nine-step absorber.

Using the atlas and tables, two or three (if possible) fairly intense lines of each of the elements being determined, and lines of the standard element should be found in the spectrograms. The line pairs selected should be homologous, i.e. both lines should be spark or arc lines and should have similar excitation energies.

The lines should be marked on the plate, and their degrees of blackening should be measured with a microphotometer (where necessary allowing for background near the lines), and characteristic curves should be drawn for each line to determine the normal blackening range. In all the spectrograms the steps of the absorber should be found where the spectral lines selected are in the normal blackening range. Since the concentrations of the elements being determined may vary in the analysis specimens, the steps and regimes selected should be those in which, on change in the concentration of the elements being determined within the necessary limits, the degrees of blackening of the lines of these elements remain within the normal exposure range.

Roughly we can proceed on the basis of the following calculations. Suppose that the spectral line intensity is directly proportional to the concentration of the element being determined. Knowing the concentration of the impurity in the specimen selected for investigation and the minimum possible concentration of the impurity, we can determine the extent to which the concentration alters. The spectral line intensity of the element being determined will also alter to the same extent (in the case of specimens of closely similar composition). We can find the logarithm of the number indicating the factor by which the line intensity alters. Multiplying this by the contrast coefficient γ, we get the extent of the variation in the degrees of blackening of these lines in relation to the minimum impurity concentrations. We then know (from the characteristic curve) whether the degree of blackening of the line will be located in the rectilinear section of the characteristic curve. Similar calculations can also be carried out for the specimen with the maximum concentration of the element being determined.

Let us suppose, for instance, that for a specimen containing 4 per cent of lead we get a degree of blackening of the line Pb 2873 Å $S = 0{\cdot}80$. The minimum content of lead in the analysis specimens is 2 per cent. For the line mentioned $\gamma = 1{\cdot}2$. The lead concentration in the specimen with the minimum lead content, is half that in the initial specimen. Thus the line intensity also falls by a half: log 2 = 0·30; γ (0·30) = (1·2) (0·30) = 0·36. The blackening of the lead line falls by 0·36 and for the specimen containing 2 per cent of lead will be 0·80–0·36 = 0·44. We can tell from the characteristic curve for the lead line Pb 2873 Å whether the blackening S = 0·44 lies within the normal blackening range.

Finally, we select regimes and steps of the absorber that give the required degrees of blackening of the spectral lines. It may be that the regimes selected will not suffice, because in the case of some of the elements being determined, all the lines will be outside the normal blackening range. If the lines lie in this range under one of the regimes and in the under-exposed range under another of the regimes, then the intermediate regimes should be tried.

Let us suppose that for the chromium lines in a sample of carbon steel on photographing the spectrum in an arc we get at a current of 4 A under-exposures with the minimum concentrations and at a current of 8 A over-exposures with the maximum contents of chromium in the analysis specimens. The spectra of the specimen being studied should then be photographed at the intermediate currents, 5, 6 and 7 A, and the most suitable regime should be selected, i.e. that under which the chromium lines lie in the normal blackening range throughout the range of variation in the chromium concentration.

Suppose for example that the degrees of blackening of the silicon lines of Silumin specimens are high under a high-voltage spark regime (C = 0·01 μF, L = 0·05 mH, I = 1·5 A) and low under the regime with C = 0·005 μF, L = 0·05 mH, I = 0·8 A. The intermediate regimes for photographing the spectra are then: 1) C = 0·005 μF, L = 0·01 mH, I = 0·8 A; 2) C = 0·005 μF, L = 0, I = 0·8 A; 3) C = 0·01 μF, L = 0·15 mH, I = 1·5 A. The most suitable of these regimes should be selected.

If the degrees of blackening of the elements are small under all the regimes, then either the regime with the greatest power of the individual discharges should be selected, or else the exposure time should be increased.

Suppose that we have found a suitable regime (or regimes), under which normal blackening of all the analysis line pairs can be obtained within the limits of variation in the concentrations of the elements being determined when the step of the absorber transmitting 25 per cent of the light from the source is used. The exposure time then has to be shortened so as to obtain the necessary degrees of blackening on photographing the spectra without using the absorber. In practice in spectral analysis it can be reckoned that the amount of illumination remains unchanged if the intensity of the light is increased to the same extent as the exposure time is decreased. Thus, if we get the required blackening with the step of the absorber transmitting 25 per cent of the light, then without introducing weakening we can get the same blackening by using an exposure amounting to 25 per cent of the exposure used in the case of the spectra photographed with weakening. And, generally speaking, the percentage of light transmitted by the step of an absorber at a given exposure time is the same as the percentage of this exposure time that is required when weakening is not introduced, to obtain the same blackening. This principle is useful in selecting the required exposure time.

It is sometimes necessary to determine large concentrations of certain elements and small concentrations of other elements simultaneously. In such cases it is often impossible to get degrees of blackening for all the analysis lines lying within the normal blackening range. In such cases it may be very useful to employ a three-step absorber. Then the analysis line pairs of the elements present in small concentrations in the specimens, can be measured photometrically without introducing weakening; the blackening of the elements present in large concentrations on the other hand, can be measured with weakening.

Selection of Heating or Sparking Time

After selecting the light source regime we have to determine the preliminary heating time in the arc or the sparking time in the spark. As a result of this determination the ratio of the intensities of the analysis line pairs can be made constant with time. In the case of arc sources heating is generally completed in several seconds, and it is usually not continued after this. In the case of spark sources, sparking is a more prolonged process.

The heating or sparking time is determined experimentally. In determining the sparking time it is desirable to work with two standard specimens containing different concentrations of the elements being determined. The specta of these specimens should be photographed at regular intervals, the intervals amounting from one-half to one-third of the exposure time selected. The first spectrum should be photographed at the moment that the spark is switched on. With the source burning continuously, the plate-holder should be moved rapidly 1 or 2 mm (depending on the height of the diaphragm aperture), and the second spectrum should then be photographed, repeating this operation in photographing the other spectra. This process is usually continued for 3–5 min, with continuous sparking. To improve the accuracy of the results, such groups of spectra should be photographed two or three times, putting a new permanent electrode over the cleaned surface of the specimen each time.

The degrees of blackening of the analysis line pairs of all the elements being determined should be measured photometrically, and the differences in blackening corresponding to each pair should be determined, in each of the spectrograms. Then graphs should be drawn correlating the differences in blackening and the time, for the analysis pairs of all the elements (Fig. 67). If the degrees of blackening of some lines lie in the under-exposure range, more sensitive plates can be used to study the sparking process, or else the intensity can be used instead of the blackening.

Sparking is considered to be complete when the graph runs parallel with the time axis (Fig. 67). The sparking time t_1 may differ in the case of the different elements being determined. It may also be found that sparking

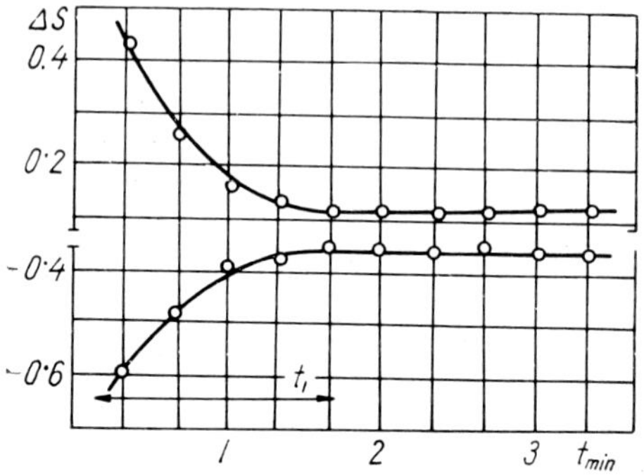

FIG. 67. Curves of sparking.

is completed earlier with one of the elements than with another. In subsequent work the longest sparking time should be used. Excessive shortening of the sparking time may lead to errors in analysis, and is thus undesirable.

Estimating the Concentration Sensitivity

One of the most important stages in developing spectral analysis procedures is the estimation of the concentration sensitivity. This estimation can be carried out to advantage during the process of selecting the electrical regime of the light source and the analysis line pairs, and also in studying the sparking process. This saves time and work, and enables unsatisfactory line pairs or electrical regimes to be eliminated.

The concentration sensitivity depends on the slope of the calibration curve: the greater the slope, the greater is the concentration sensitivity and the less reliably can the differences be established in the concentrations of the element being determined. In photographing two specimens with different contents of the elements being determined, it is easy to determine the analysis pairs and the regimes having the greater concentration sensitivity, on the basis of the calibration curve drawn from the two points. We will illustrate this with an example.

Suppose that in order to determine the content of lead in bronzes we have selected the two analysis line pairs Pb 2873–Cu 2882 Å and Pb 2833–Cu 2824 Å. In the horizontal sections of the sparking curves obtained for these line pairs, we have found for the two specimens the differences in blackenings ΔS_{I} and ΔS_{II}. For the line pair Pb 2873–Cu 2882 Å $\Delta S_{I} = -0{\cdot}70$ and $\Delta S_{II} = -1{\cdot}10$ and the difference $\Delta S_{II} - \Delta S_{I} = 0{\cdot}60 = \delta\Delta S$. For the pair Pb 2883–Cu 2824 Å we get $\Delta S_{I} = -0{\cdot}50$, $\Delta S_{II} = -0{\cdot}20$ and $\delta\Delta S = 0{\cdot}30$. We have found that in the case of an identical variation in the lead concentration the difference in blackening varies twice as quickly in the case of one analysis line pair than in the case of the other line pair. The concentration sensitivity, which we can characterize by the quantity $\delta\Delta S$, is obviously notably greater in the case of the first pair. By comparing the two light source regimes on the basis of the $\delta\Delta S$-value determined for a single line pair, we can find which of their concentration sensitivities is the greater.

In subsequent work the analysis line pairs and the regimes where the concentration sensitivity is low (the slope of the calibration curve is far less than 45°) will not be considered. Thus it may become necessary to go over to the selection of a new light-source regime or other analysis line pairs. By estimating the concentration sensitivity this can be foreseen in good time.

After selection of the sparking time, the spectra of the standards should be photographed three times under the regimes selected. Each spectrum is photographed after preliminary sparking of the sample. The source burns continuously during the sparking and the exposure times. The spectrograph shutter is closed during sparking and open during exposure.

Photometric measurement is carried out on the analysis line pairs in the photographed spectra, and the calibration curves are drawn. Two or three curves should be drawn for one of the elements being evaluated, and of these the one should be selected that has the steepest slope and the minimum scatter of the points relative to the calibration straight line.

It may be that the curve with the steepest slope has a considerable scatter, while the points of a curve with a shallow slope lie closer to the calibration straight line. In such cases, it is advisable to base the analysis on the curve with a slightly less steep slope. The curves obtained for the other elements being evaluated, are selected in the same way.

In developing spectral analysis procedures the graphs can be drawn within the coordinates log I_x/I_0 and log C. In this way it is possible to work within a wider range of intensities, and also to use lines with different contrast coefficients, for comparison purposes.

Estimating the Analysis Accuracy

In order to determine the accuracy of the procedure adopted, it is necessary to find out how accurately the concentrations of the elements can be determined, viz. the size of the analysis error. This depends on the accuracy of shaping and setting the electrodes, the lighting system, the stability of the light source under the analysis regime adopted, the non-uniformity of the photographic plates, and also the errors permissible in making photometric measurements of the blackening of the spectral lines and in plotting the calibration curve. By adding together all the permissible errors, the error involved in determining the concentration of the element being studied can be assessed.

The errors may be accidental or systematic errors. In the case of accidental errors the measurements may give results that differ from the true ones and are on the high or the low side. Systematic errors may arise in the spectral analysis of alloys, when the standards and the analysis samples differ in their structure, in the shape of the electrodes, and in their mass; such errors may also be due to inaccuracies in the chemical analysis of the samples or the presence of "third bodies" in the samples or the standards. Systematic errors should be eliminated or allowed for.

Usually when the correct procedure is followed, only accidental errors are found. The arithmetic sum of these errors in multiple measurements approaches zero. The measurement error in this case is determined by the reproducibility of the results obtained.

To determine the error of the procedure adopted, spectral analysis should be carried out not less than 20 times on a sample where the concentration of the elements have been found by chemical methods (one of the standards can be used). For each of the elements we thus get 20 values of the concentration, which are determined with a greater or smaller degree of accuracy. For each measurement of the concentration we find the difference between it and the results of the chemical analysis of the standard. These differences are the absolute errors of the spectral analysis. Let us suppose for example that the content of manganese in a steel sample is 1 per cent, and that the spectral analysis gave the results shown in Table 40. In order to find the arithmetic mean of the absolute error, it is necessary, without paying attention to the sign, to find the sum of the absolute errors of the spectral analyses and to divide this by the number of measurements.*

* Sometimes the probable and the mean square error are referred to in the literature.[1, 3, 86] The mean probable error m is the arithmetic mean error multiplied by 0·83, and it simply denotes that half the measurements were made at an error not exceeding the mean probable error. The mean square error r equals the arithmetic mean error multiplied by 1·25. To

TABLE 40.

Content of manganese, %	Absolute error, %	Content of manganese, %	Absolute error, %
1·05	+0·05	1·01	+0·01
1·01	+0·01	1·02	+0·02
0·93	−0·07	0·98	−0·02
1·00	0	1·04	+ 0·04
0·97	−0·03	0·96	−0·04
1·02	+0·02	1·00	0
1·03	+0·03	0·97	−0·03
0·94	−0·06	1·03	+0·03
0·99	−0·01	0·96	−0·04
1·06	+0·06	1·02	+0·02

In our example the absolute arithmetic mean error is:

$$\varrho = \frac{0{\cdot}05+0{\cdot}01+0{\cdot}07+0+0{\cdot}03+0{\cdot}02+0{\cdot}03+0{\cdot}06+0{\cdot}01+0{\cdot}06+0{\cdot}01}{20}$$

$$\frac{+0{\cdot}02+0{\cdot}02+0{\cdot}04+0{\cdot}04+0+0{\cdot}03+0{\cdot}03+0{\cdot}04+0{\cdot}02}{20} = 0{\cdot}03\%$$

The measurement error cannot be characterized completely by the size of the absolute error. In estimating this error the concentrations at which a given error was obtained, should be taken into account. Thus, for example, if the mean absolute error in determining silicon in aluminium alloys is 0·1 per cent then at a silicon content of 5 per cent in the sample this error is small, but at a silicon content of 0·5 per cent it is large. Thus the accuracy of quantitative spectral analysis is usually characterized on the basis of the size of the relative error, determined from the equation

$$\varepsilon = \frac{\varrho}{C} 100\%$$

where C is the concentration of the element being evaluated in the sample. In the example given above the relative error is: for 5 per cent silicon:

$$\varepsilon = \frac{0{\cdot}1\%}{5\%} 100\% = 2\%$$

calculate this, the squares of the absolute errors are added together and the result is divided by the number of measurements minus one. Then square root of the expression obtained is determined.

for 0·5 per cent of silicon:

$$\varepsilon = \frac{0{\cdot}1\%}{0{\cdot}5\%}\,100\% = 20\%$$

In the example given earlier, with manganese, the mean relative error is:

$$\varepsilon = \frac{0{\cdot}03\%}{1\%}\,100\% = 3\%$$

If the analysis errors are not very great, the mean relative error can be found from the difference in the degrees of blackening ΔS. For this, the spectra of one of the samples should be photographed not less than 20 times. The differences in blackening and their arithmetic mean ΔS_{mean} are found from the photometric data of the analysis line pair of the given element. Then the deviations of the differences in the degrees of blackening from their mean value $\delta\Delta S = \Delta S - \Delta S_{\text{mean}}$ are determined for all the spectrograms. The arithmetic mean of these deviations is:

$$\varrho_0 = \frac{\delta\Delta S_1 + \delta\Delta S_2 + \ldots + \delta\Delta S_n}{n}$$

This quantity is connected with the mean relative error of the analysis, expressed as a percentage, by the relation:

$$\varepsilon = 2{\cdot}3\,\frac{\varrho_0}{\gamma b}\,100\% = 230\,\frac{\varrho_0}{K}\,\%$$

The coefficient $K = \gamma b$ is equal to the tangent of the angle of slope of the calibration curve. Thus, if the arithmetic mean error ϱ_0 in the quantities ΔS is 0·03 and the tangent of the angle of slope of the calibration curve is $K = 1{\cdot}2$, then:

$$\varepsilon = 230\,\frac{0{\cdot}03}{1{\cdot}2}\,\% = 5{\cdot}8\%$$

The spectral analysis procedure can be considered to be satisfactory if the elements being evaluated are determined with an error corresponding to an arithmetic mean error of 3–5 per cent. In a single determination we may obtain a greater deviation from the true value. But if we take the mean result of several measurements, then the size of the relative error will fall, in inverse proportion to the square root of the number of measurements. If the relative error for a single measurement equals ε, then the relative error for n measurements will be:

$$\varepsilon_n = \frac{\varepsilon}{\sqrt{n}}$$

For example, if we have a relative error of 6 per cent in a single measurement, and analysis has to be carried out at a relative error of 3 per cent, then we should photograph each analysis sample four times:

$$\varepsilon = 6\%; \ \varepsilon_n = 3\%,$$

$$n = \frac{\varepsilon}{\varepsilon_n} = 2; \quad \text{hence } n = 4.$$

It should be borne in mind that the size of the relative accidental error will not fall indefinitely. It is limited by the instrumental errors.

For example, the degrees of blackening of spectral lines are usually measured to within an accuracy of 0·005. When the calibration curve has a slope of 45° this error of the microphotometer will lead to an unavoidable error of about 1 per cent in determining the concentrations:

$$\varepsilon = 230\frac{0{\cdot}005}{1}\% \approx 1\%$$

Under these conditions it is pointless to reduce the error to below 1 per cent by averaging a large number of results.

In practice in spectral analysis, the mean is taken of two or three measurements of the quantities ΔS. Here it is not always possible to discard one of three measurements when it is appreciably different from the others. If, in photographing the spectrum with the "erroneous" ΔS-value we did not make any omissions (the electrodes were shaped correctly, the sparking and exposure times were the correct ones, etc.) , then the ΔS-value cannot be discarded and the analysis should be carried out once more. It should be borne in mind that the permissible error also depends on the skill and experience of the analyst.

2. ANALYSIS OF LOW-ALLOY STEELS

The analysis of low-alloy steels can be carried out with spark or arc excitation of the spectrum. Slightly more reproducible results can be obtained using a high-voltage spark discharge. But with this light source the photography time is two to four times as long as that on operation with an a.c. arc. Thus the light source should be selected in relation to the required accuracy and speed of the analysis. In particular, the analysis of steels during melting should be carried out with an a.c. arc.

Procedure for Analysing Carbon and Low-alloy Steels with Arc Excitation of the Spectrum(44)

The light source is a DG-1 (DG-2) arc generator with a current of 5A. The current in the maintaining circuit is 0·2 A, the distance between the electrodes is 1·5 mm, the discharge gap is 0·6–0·8 mm long. The permanent electrode consists of rods of pure copper (M 1) diameter 6–8 mm, wedge-shaped with a working area 1·5–2·0 mm in diameter. Permanent electrodes of spectrally pure carbons can also be used. In this case the electrodes are made wedge-shaped with an angle of about 45° and a working area 2–2·5 mm in diameter. But the reproducibility of the results is lower with carbon than with copper electrodes. The standards can be samples of steels of the 12th and 5th sets of standards, produced by the Urals Metal Institute.

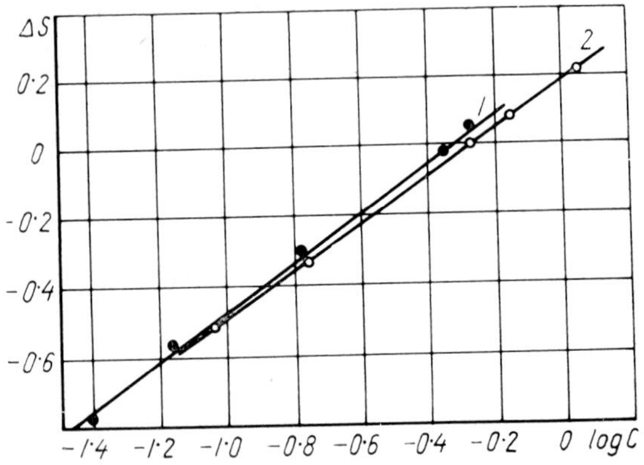

FIG. 68. Calibration curves for determining (*1*) nickel and (*2*) manganese in carbon steel.

The spectra are photographed with an ISP-22 (ISP-28) spectrograph with a three-lens standard system of illumination. The slit width of the spectrograph is 0·015 mm. The heating time is 10 sec. When type I spectrographic plates are used (sensitivity 0·5–1·0 GOST units), the exposure time is 40–60 sec; three spectra are photographed for each sample.

The photographic plates are developed in a standard metal-hydroquinone developer, needing 3 min. The developer should be at a temperature of 12–20° C After rinsing, the plate should be fixed in acid fixing solution.

To speed up analysis it is advisable to use the visual photometric interpolation method described earlier. The calibration curves should be plotted within the coordinates log I_x/I_{Fe} and log C. To eliminate the need for photographing the spectra of standards on each plate, it is advisable to use a permanent calibration curve. To plot this curve 15 to 18 spectra of each standard should be photographed (on five or six plates), using a nine-step absorber. The mean value of log I_x/I_{Fe} from all 15 to 18 spectra should be plotted on the curve.

In order to check the position of the curve, one or two standards should be photographed each day on alternate plates.

When a permanent curve is used, the conditions of photographing the spectrograms must be rigorously adhered to. The required accuracy can only be attained with practice and experience. Thus during the first few months it is advisable to photograph one control standard on each plate. In this standard the concentrations of all the elements should be about in the middle of the range of concentrations being evaluated. When the 12th set of standards of the Urals Metals Institute is being used, the standard No. 125 can be taken as the control standard. The degrees of blackening of the analysis line pairs in the spectra of the standards and the samples, shown in Table 41, are measured on an MF-2 microphotometer. The basic, and also the working graphs for each alternate plate, are plotted according to the system laid down ~~on page~~ above.

TABLE 41.

Wavelengths of lines, Å		Concentration range, %
of element being evaluated	of standard element (Fe)	
Mn 2933·1	2920·7	0·20 – 1·20
Si 2528·5	2530·7	0·03 – 0·50
Si 2881·6	2869·3	0·01 – 0·50
Cr 2677·2	2684·8	0·02 – 1·20
Ni 3050·8	3055·3	0·05 – 1·20
Al 3092·7	3055·3	0·01 – 0·30
Mo 3170·4	3178·0	0·01 – 0·30
Ti 3088·0	3055·3	0·02 – 0·30

Procedure for Analysing Steels with Spark Excitation of the Spectrum[45]

The spark is obtained from an IG-2 (IG-3) generator with complex connexion. The capacitance of the discharge gap is 0·01 μF, the self induction is 0·01 mH the auxiliary gap is 3 mm, the distance between the electrodes is 2 mm. The current in the primary circuit of the transformer is 1·4–1·6 A (one discharge per half-cycle of the current). The permanent electrodes are rods of spectrally pure carbon 6 mm in diameter, wedge-shaped with a working area 1 mm in diameter. The standards are samples of the 5th set of the Urals Metals Institute.

The spectra are photographed by an ISP-22 (ISP-28) spectrograph, at a slit width of 0·015 mm. The plates are diapositive or Type 1 "spectrographic", with a sensitivity of 0·5–0·7 GOST units. With the ISP-22 spectrograph using

PS-162 stands, the use of lighting without condensers is recommended. The distance between the source and the spectrograph slit is 15–25 cm. This distance should be selected with accuracy if normal degrees of blackening of the analysis line pairs are to be obtained. The heating time is 1 min, the exposure time 1 min. The spectrum of each sample is photographed three times. The photographic plates are processed in standard solutions.

By means of an MF-2 microphotometer (slit width 0·2 mm) the degrees of blackening of the following analysis line pairs are measured: Mn 2933·1–Fe 2936·9 Å; Si 2881·6–Fe 2880·8 Å; Cu 3274·0–Fe 3286·8 Å; Cr 2677·2–Fe 2689·2 Å; Mo 2816·2–Fe 2829·6 Å; Ti 3349·0–Fe 3255·9 Å; Ni 3414·8–Fe 3399·3 Å.

The curves are plotted according to the three-standard method. If it is impossible to draw a straight line so that the points corresponding to the standards lie within 0·025 of it according to the ΔS scale, then the curve should be rejected. If one of the three values differs from the others by more than 0·05 then it should also be rejected. When the procedure is carried out correctly the arithmetic mean analysis error does not exceed 2 per cent of the content of the element in the sample.

Determination of Carbon in Steels

The determination of carbon in steels by chemical methods can be carried out fairly rapidly and accurately. But in some cases, especially in determining carbon in finished parts, chemical methods are unsatisfactory for carrying out local analyses.

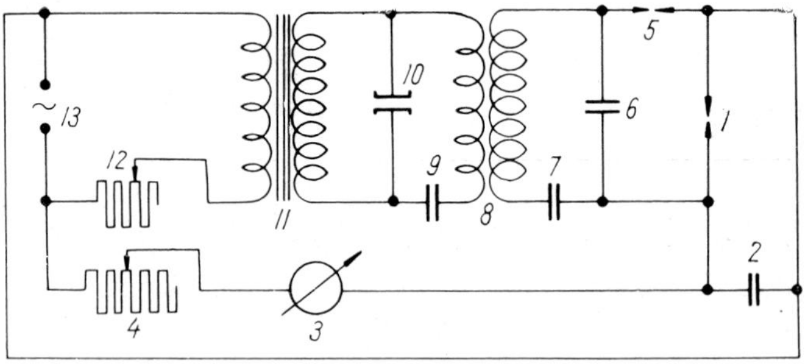

FIG. 69. Electrical diagram of low-voltage spark generator with maximum self-induction.

1—analysis gap; *2*—30-40 μF capacitor; *3*—ammeter; *4*—spark rheostat; *5*—discharger; *6*—high-voltage condenser; *7*—blocking capacitor; *8*—air-cored transformer; 9—high-frequency circuit capacitor; *10*—high-frequency discharger; *11*—transformer; *12*—transformer rheostat; *13*—a.c. mains terminals.

The determination of carbon by spectral analysis presents some difficulty. The carbon spectrum is poor in lines suitable for analysis purposes. Moreover these lines can only be excited in spark light sources. It is also well-known that carbon burns away rapidly in the zone of action of an electrical discharge.(29)

A number of methods have been proposed for the quantitative spectrographic analysis of carbon in steels. In most methods the recommended light source is a high-frequency spark, or sometimes a low-frequency high-voltage spark. The best results are obtained with a high-frequency spark with a magnesium permanent electrode.(46) In Ref. 46 carbon concentrations of as low as 0·01 per cent were determined successfully.

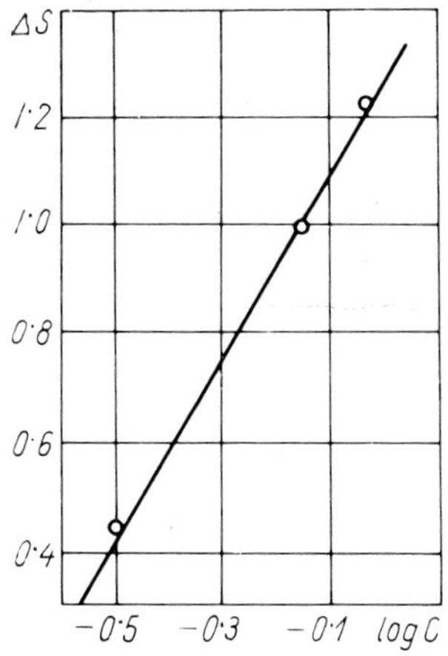

FIG. 70. Typical calibration straight line for determination of carbon by means of low-voltage spark.

In order to determine carbon in the concentration range 0·1–1 per cent, we have for several years tried out a method with excitation of the spectrum by a low-voltage spark. The spark can easily be obtained from a PS-39 generator with the diagram shown in Fig. 69.(71) The capacitance of the discharge circuit is 30–40 μF, the inductance is the minimum, the current is 3 A, the analysis gap is 0·75 to 1 mm. The sparking stability depends on the high-frequency spark of the maintaining circuit. The current in the primary winding of the transformer *11* is 0·5 A, the gap between the plates of the discharger *10* equ als 0·9 mm, the gap in the discharger is 5–10 mm. On the basis of the work done in Ref. 46, a cylindrical magnesium permanent electrode 2·0 mm in diameter is used.

The spectra are photographed with an ISP-28 (ISP-22) spectrograph with a standard three-lens lighting system. The slit-width of the spectrograph is 0·015 mm. The sparking time is 10 sec. When Type III photographic plates are used, with a sensitivity of 5·5 GOST units, the exposure time is 45 sec. The standards are the 12th set of carbon steels of the Urals Metals Institute.

The degrees of blackening of the carbon line C 2296·9 Å are measured by means of an MF-2 microphotometer. The line Fe 2307·3 Å is used for comparison purposes. The ΔS-values are determined as the mean of three measurements.

The curve is plotted by the three-standard method. A typical calibration curve is shown in Fig. 70. The tangent of the angle of slope of the calibration straight line $\gamma b = 1{\cdot}5$. In analysing samples containing 0·1–0·3 per cent of carbon, a separate curve should be plotted. Its slope is about 45° ($\gamma b \approx 1$).

The error in making a single determination of carbon by the method described, does not exceed 6–7 per cent of the size of the concentration being measured.

Determination of Phosphorus in Steels

The determination of phosphorus in steels by chemical methods is more lengthy and difficult than the determination of carbon, and cannot always be carried out accurately. Thus the possibility of the spectral analysis of phosphorus is a great advantage.

The method presented below has been used for five years at the Minsk Bearing Factory,[(47)] and is not basically different from that proposed in Ref. 46.

The light source is an a.c. current (DG-1 or DG-2 generator). The current is 10 A, the size of the gap is 2·5 mm. The permanent electrode is a carbon rod 6 mm in diameter, ground hemispherical at the end. The spectra are photographed with an ISP-22 (ISP-28) spectrograph. The slit-width of the spectrograph is 0·015 mm. A PS-197 condenser is used for photography; this is placed 160 mm from the slit, while the electrodes are 250 mm from the slit. On using Type III photographic plates, sensitivity 5·5 GOST units, the exposure time is 45 sec. No heating is carried out. The standards are taken from routine analysis samples.

The calibration curve is plotted according to the three-standard method. The analysis line pair is P 2149·1–Fe 2150·2 Å. When the samples contain more than 0·5 per cent of copper, it is difficult to determine the phosphorus, because the line Cu 2149·0 Å is superimposed on line P 2149·1 Å.

ANALYSIS OF CAST IRONS

Cast irons are the commonest objects of analysis in iron and steel, mechanical engineering and machine-tool works. Mostly manganese and silicon, but sometimes also chromium and nickel are determined in cast irons. The contents of chromium and nickel are small, and it is best to evaluate them with an a.c. arc. In this way the manganese and silicon contents can be found from the same spectrograms. The method of analysing grey cast irons with arc excitation of the spectrum, has been used successfully for a number of years in the spectral analysis laboratory of the Minsk Bearing Factory.

The arc is produced in a DG-1 (DG-2) generator; the current is 5 A. The size of the discharge gap is 0·7 mm, the distance between the electrodes is 1·5 mm. The permanent electrode is a wedge-shaped copper electrode, diameter 6–8 mm, with a working area 1·5–2 mm in diameter. The standards are taken from production samples; their quantitative composition is found by repeated chemical analysis. To determine silicon and manganese the 19th set of standards of foundry iron the Urals Metals Institute, can be used.

The spectra are photographed with an ISP-22 (ISP-28) spectrograph, with a standard three-lens lighting system. The slit-width of the spectrograph is 0·015 mm. The photographic plates are diapositive or Type I spectrographic plates (sensitivity 0·5 to 1 GOST units). The heating time is 10 sec. To obtain normal degrees of blackening of the analysis line pairs, the exposure varies between 15 and 40 sec. The degrees of blackening of the following line pairs: Si 2514·3–Fe 2518·1 Å; Ma 2933·1–Fe 2926·6 Å; Ni 3050·8–Fe 3053·1 Å; Cr 2849·3–Fe 2845·5 Å are measured by the objective photometry method (MF-2 microphotometer). The difference between the degrees of blackening of these analysis pairs, is related graphically to the logarithm of the concentration of the corresponding element, by the three-standard method.

Manganese and silicon in grey cast irons can also be determined with spark excitation of the spectrum. An IG-3 (IG-2) generator is used with complex connexion. The capacitance of the discharge circuit is 0·02 μF, the self-induction coil is disconnected ($L = 0$), the voltage in the primary winding of the transformer is 220 V, the current is 3·5–4 A. The distance between the electrodes is 3 mm. The sparking time is 45–60 sec, the exposure is 30–60 sec., depending on the sensitivity of the photographic materials. The other conditions are the same as on operation with an a.c. arc. The silicon is determined on the basis of the line pair Si 2516·1–Fe 2518·1 Å, the manganese on the basis of the pair Mn 2939·3–Fe 2926·6 Å. The manganese line mentioned can also be compared with the iron line Fe 2936·9 Å.

The following method[44] is recommended for use in analysing cast irons for steel manufacture containing a larger amount of manganese and a smaller amount of silicon than grey cast-irons (Mn 0·80 – 4·40 per cent, Si 0·20–1·50 per cent). An IG-3 (IG-2) spark generator is used with complex connexion. The capacitance of the discharge circuit is 0·01 μF, the inductance is 0·01 mH, the voltage is 220 V, the current is 1·4–1·6 A (one discharge per half cycle of the current). The permanent electrodes are wedge-shaped rods of electrolytic copper 6–8 mm in diameter with a working area 1 mm in diameter. The standards can be taken from the 18th set of standards of the Urals Metals Institute. The length of the auxiliary gap is 3 mm, the analysis gap is 2 mm. The sparking time is 45 sec, the exposure 45–60 sec. The conditions for photographing the spectra and treating the plates, are similar to those described above.

The analysis line pairs are: Mn 2889·6–Fe 2883·7 Å and Si 2516·1–Fe 2518·1 Å. The calibration curve is plotted according to the three-standard method.

When rapid analyses have to be made of cast irons, the photometric-interpolation method can be used. The analysis time can be greatly reduced (to 17–20 min) by using the permanent-graph method or else the control-standard method.

The accuracy of the analysis of cast irons by spectral methods complies with the specifications laid down by GOST for accelerated and marking analyses.

4. Analysis of High-alloy Steels

Of the wide variety of high-alloy steels it is the chromium–nickel alloys of the type Ya 1T and the high-speed steels that have to be analysed most frequently.

High-speed steels are analysed with the medium-dispersion ISP-28 or ISP-22 spectrographs with a standard three-lens lighting system. The slit-width of the spectrograph is 0·015 mm. The plates are diapositive or Type I spectrographic with a sensitivity of 0·5–1 GOST units.

The spectra are excited by means of a high-voltage spark from an IG-3 (IG-2) generator with complex connexion. The capacitance is 0·01 μF, the inductance 0·01 mH. The current is 2·5–3·0 A (stable sparking is obtained at two discharges per half-cycle of the current). The length of the auxiliary gap is 3 mm, the analysis gap is 2 mm. The permanent electrodes are wedge-shaped copper rods 6–8 mm in diameter, with a working area of 1·5–2 mm. The sparking time is 30 sec, the exposure 20–40 sec, depending on the sensitivity of the photographic materials.

To plot the curves by the three-standard method the 6th set of standards of the Urals Metals Institute is used. The analysis line pairs are: V 3063·2–Fe 3062·2 Å; W 2397·1–Fe 2396·7 Å; Mn 2939·3–Fe 2936·9 Å; No 2816·2–Fe 2828·8 Å; Cr 2792·1–Fe 2993·9 Å.

The method described above is also suitable for the analysis of type Ya 1 T chromium–nickel steels, using the 9th set of standards of the Urals Metals Institute. Manganese, nickel, chromium and silicon are determined on the basis of the following line pairs: Mn 2939·3–Fe 2936·9 Å; Ni 2416·1–Fe 2417·9 Å; Cr 2792·1–Fe 2793·9 Å; Si 2516·1–Fe 2518·1 Å.

The accuracy of the determination of silicon by the method described is not great. Therefore chromium–nickel steels are often analysed using an a.c. arc to excite the spectra (DG-1 or DG-2 generator). The arc current is 4·5–5 A. The length of the analysis discharge gap is 1·5 mm. The length of the auxiliary discharge gap is 0·7 mm. The heating time is 10 sec, the exposure time is 15 sec. The analysis line pairs are: Mn 2939–Fe 2936·9 Å; Si 2516·1–Fe 2518·1 Å; Ni 2992·6–Fe 2991·6 Å; Cr 2553·1–Fe 2621·7 Å.

It should be borne in mind that when there is a sharp increase in the total quantity of alloying elements, the content of iron in the sample changes appreciably. The intensity of the standard time then falls, and the curve representing high concentrations of the alloying elements bends upwards. This case is illustrated in Fig. 71. Curve *1* is plotted within the coordinates ΔS, $\log C$, curve *2* is plotted according to the same data with allowance being made for the fall in the concentration of the iron. The method used to allow for the diluting effect of the alloying elements is briefly described on page 107.

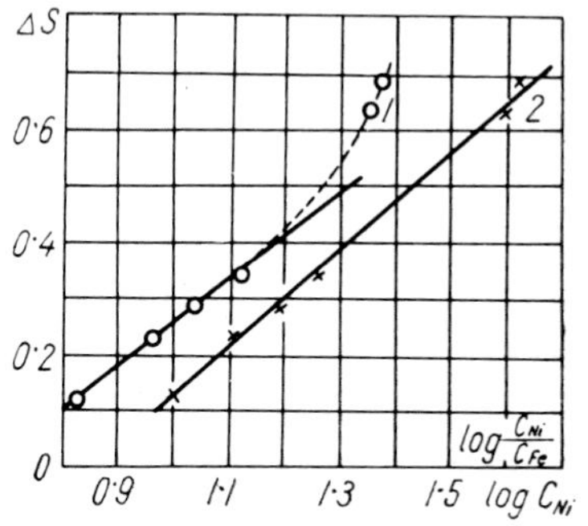

FIG. 71. Calibration curves for determination of nickel in high-alloy steels.
1—in coordinates ΔS, $\log C_{Ni}$; *2*—in coordinates ΔS, $\log \frac{C_{Ni}}{C_{Fe}}$

Systematic errors may often arise in the analysis of high-alloy steels because of differences in the structure of the samples and standards. Thus, before proceeding with spectral analysis the structure of the samples and standards should be checked in the metallographic laboratory. In practice small differences in their structure can be eliminated by prolonging the preliminary sparking time. But, in order to be certain of the accuracy of the spectral determinations, the results should be checked at an early stage with the results of chemical analyses.

In addition to the alloy steels discussed above, it is also necessary to analyse various other grades of steel. The main obstacle to the development or the implementation of the new method, is the absence of standards.

The problem of obtaining standards can be simplified by using the parallel-curve method.(48—50) According to this method, additions of other alloying elements or increases in the concentrations of the alloying elements lead to parallel shifting of the curves relative to the calibration straight lines drawn for alloys of less complicated composition. If an alloy brought to the laboratory for analysis does not differ substantially from the grades of steel being analysed,

TABLE 42. SPECTRAL LINES USED TO EVALUATE ALLOYING ELEMENTS AND IMPURITIES IN STEELS AND CAST IRONS

Element being evaluated	Range of concentrations, %	Wavelengths of lines, Å	Excitation energy of lines, eV
1	2	3	4
Aluminium	0·2 – 4	I 3082·2	4·02
	0·01 – 0·3	I 3092·7	4·02
	0·2 – 2	I 3944·0	3·14
	0·02 – 2	I 3961·5	3·14
Arsenic	0·01 – 0·3	I 2288·1	–
	0·08 – 0·40	I 2349·8	–
Boron	0·001 – 0·1	I 2089·6	5·94
	0·001 – 1	I 2496·8	4·96
	0·001 – 0·1	I 2497·7	4·96
Calcium	0·02 – 0·6	II 3933·7	9·26
Carbon	0·05 – 3·0	III 2296·9	–
Chromium	10 – 25	I 2653·6	–
	0·02 – 3	II 2677·2	–
	10 – 25	2773·3	–
	0·2 – 2	2830·5	–
	0·5 – 2	II 2849·8	–
	10 – 25	2853·2	–
	2 – 20	II 2860·9	–
	1 – 20	II 2682·6	–
	0·3 – 25	II 3128·7	13·16
	0·3 – 25	II 3147·2	13·18
Cobalt	0·7 – 48	I 2411·6	5·24
	0·5 – 50	I 2414·5	5·30
	0·7 – 48	2420·7	–
	4·5	II 2580·3	13·90
	0·7 – 48	2648·6	–
	0·7 – 48	3072·3	4·21
Copper	0·1 – 1·5	I 3247·5	3·82
	~0·25%	I 3274·0	3·78
Magnesium	0·01 0·3	II 2795·5	12·08
	0·01 – 0·3	II 2802·7	12·07

Element being evaluated	Range of concentrations, %	Wavelengths of lines, Å	Excitation energy, of lines, eV
1	2	3	4
Manganese	0·2–2	II 2576·1	12·24
	0·1–1·2	II 2593·7	12·20
	1–10	2815·0	–
	0·2–2	2933·1	–
	0·1–2	2939·3	–
	0·3–30	II 3482·9	12·82
	0·3–30	II 3488·7	12·81
Molybdenum	2–5	2684·1	–
	0·1–4	2775·4	–
	0·1–3	II 2816·2	–
	4–7	2930·5	–
	0·01–1	I 3170·3	3·91
Nickel	1–10	II 2316·0	–
	1–10	II 2356·4	–
	0·3–20	II 2394·5	14·48
	1–4	II 2416·1	14·61
	5–55	I 2992·6	4·17
	1–20	I 3012·0	4.54
	0·05–1·2	I 3050·8	4·09
	1–5	I 3101·9	4·11
	1·5–5	I 3391·0	3·65
	0·1–4	I 3414·8	3·65
Niobium	0·1–1·5	II 3094·2	11·29
	0·1–4	II 3130·8	11·17
	0·2–1·5	II 3195·0	10·98
	0·2–1·5	II 3195·0	10·98
Phosphorus	0·025–1·0	I 2149·1	–
Silicon	0·1–2	I 2506·9	4·95
	0·2–4	I 2516·1	4·95
	0·03–0·5	I 2528·5	4·93
	0·01–0·5	I 2881·6	5·08
	0·1–5	I 3905·5	5·08
Tellurium	0·002–0·02	I 2142·8	–

Element being evaluated	Range of concentrations, %	Wavelengths of lines, Å	Excitation energy, of lines, eV
1	2	3	4
Titanium	1·5–4	I 2646·6	4·73
	0·02–3	II 3088·0	10·90
	0·2–1·5	II 3103·8	12·71
	0·2–1	II 3242·0	10·66
	0·004–3	II 3261·6	12·52
	0·01–2·5	II 3349·0	11·14
Tungsten	0·2–20	II 2397·1	13·54
	1–30	2488·8	–
	0·2–2	I 3300·8	4·36
	0·2–1	I 3881·4	3·80
Vanadium	1–3	II 2882 5	11·37
	0·1–2	II 3102·3	11·10
	0·01–2	II 3110·7	11·07
	0·001–0·02	I 3183·4	3·91
	0·01–0·2	I 3185·4	3·96
	0·05–3	I 3875·1	3·23
	> 0·2	II 3914·3	11·70

then it is sufficient to use one standard sample, which can be taken from the production samples. Its composition should be found by careful chemical analysis.

The basic calibration curve is plotted on the basis of the earlier standards for each element. The point for the standard of the new grade of alloy will be found in the same system of coordinates. The calibration straight line for the analysis of the alloy brought to the laboratory, is then drawn through this point parallel with the basic curve.

Binary alloys can also be used to draw the basic curves. These should be melted separately, and then submitted to accurate chemical analysis.

It should be noted that the method described requires critical study, because the presence of other impurities leads not only to parallel shifting of the calibration curves, but also to variation in their slope.[50]

The selection of the analysis line pairs is important in relation to obtaining the required accuracy in steel analysis. Tables 42 and 43 give the basic lines used in steel analysis.[3, 6, 7, 49] The data given in these tables may be of use in the development of new methods of steel analysis and in improving the accuracy of existing methods.

TABLE 43. SPECTRAL LINES OF IRON USED AS STANDARD LINES

Wavelengths of lines, Å	Excitation energy, eV	Wavelengths of lines, Å	Excitation energy, eV
1	2	3	4
I 2132·0	6·81	II 2511·8	15·48
2151·7	–	I 2518·1	5·01
II 2294·6	16·09	II 2525·4	15·40
II 2298·2	15·89	I 2530·7	4·98
II 2311·2	–	II 2574·4	15·26
II 2327·4	13·27	II 2577·9	13·76
I 2350·4	–	II 2587·9	16·80
II 2391·5	13·34	II 2590·5	–
II 2396·7	–	II 2591·5	13·68
II 2407·9	–	II 2630·1	15·43
II 2411·1	13·12	I 2635·8	5·69
II 2413·3	13·12	II 2649·5	–
II 2415·0	13·11	II 2684·8	16·29
II 2417·9	16·23	I 2689·2	5·52
II 2422·7	–	II 2692·8	13·45
II 2440·4	–	II 2724·9	13·45
II 2493·2	15·49	II 2730·7	13·47
I 2495·9	5·82	I 2772·1	4·56
I 2496·5	5·87	II 2779·3	15·58
I 2498·9	5·01	II 2783·7	15·56
I 2507·9	5·89	I 2804·5	5·33
II 2509·1	16·04	I 2807·0	5·33
I 2510·8	4·99	I 2813·3	5·32
I 2819·3	7·15	I 3100·7	4·95
I 2823·3	5·35	II 3116·6	15·72
2828·6	–	II 3154·2	15·55
II 2831·6	15·43	II 3167·9	15·58
I 2845·5	5·31	I 3178·0	6·30
I 2869·3	4·37	II 3187·3	15·89
I 2874.2	4·31	I 3205·4	6·35
II 2880·8	13·15	II 3255·9	12·65
I 2912·2	6·40	I 3260·0	6·24
I 2920·7	5·85	I 3286·8	5·94
II 2926·6	13·08	I 3366·9	5·87
I 2929·0	6·43	I 3392·3	5·85
I 2936·9	4·22	I 3399·3	5·84
II 2944·4	13·76	I 3407·5	5·81
I 3001·0	4·22	I 3413·1	5·82
I 3009·6	5·03	I 3443·9	3·68
I 3031·6	5·10	I 3465·9	3·68

Wavelengths of lines, Å	Excitation energy, eV	Wavelengths of lines, Å	Excitation energy, eV
1	2	3	4
I 3042·7	5·06	I 3873·8	5·63
I 3055·3	—	I 3911·0	—
I 3059·1	4·11	3913·2	—
I 3067·2	4·95	I 3927·9	3·26
I 3075·7	4·99	I 3930·3	3·24
3077·6	—	I 3964·5	5·97
I 3083·7	5·01	I 4005·2	4·65
I 3091·6	5·02	I 4009·7	5·31

5. Analysis of Aluminium-base Alloys

The spectral analysis of aluminium-base alloys is at a very advanced stage of development. Such alloys are analysed mostly by means of an IG-3 (or IG-2) high-voltage spark generator.(7) But when necessary other light sources can be used.

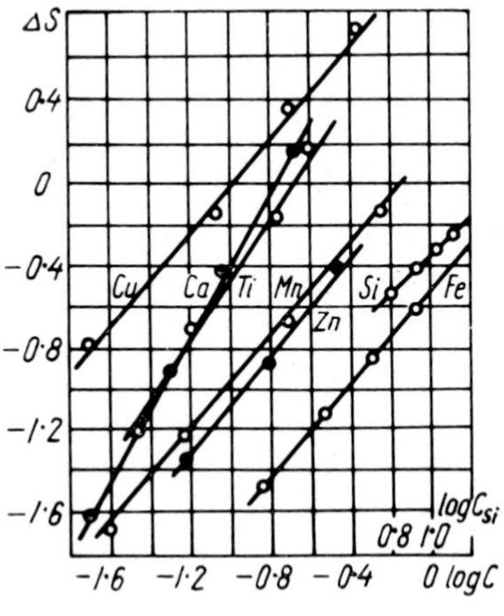

FIG. 72. Calibration curves for determination of silicon, iron, copper, manganese, titanium, zinc and calcium in Silumins.

The analysis specimens of the alloys are ground flat. The permanent electrodes are wedge-shaped rods of pure aluminium 6–8 mm in diameter with a working area 2 mm in diameter. Paired electrodes of the material being analysed can also used. The length of the analysis gap is 2·5 mm. The spectra

TABLE 44. ANALYSIS SPECTRAL LINES FOR ALUMINIUM ALLOYS

Element	Concentration, %	Wavelength, Å	Excitation energy, eV
1	2	3	4
Aluminium		II 2321·6	–
		I 2367·1	5·22
		I 2373·4	5·22
		I 2568·0	4·81
		I 2575·1	4·81
		I 2652·5	4·66
		I 2660·4	4.66
		II 2669·2	10·62
		II 2816·2	17·80
		I 3050·1	7·65
		I 3082·2	4·02
		II 3586·9	21·28
Beryllium	0·0008 – 0·2	I 2348·6	5·28
	0·005 – 0·06	II 3130·4	13·27
		I 2650·5	7·40
Chromium	0·1 – 0·4	II 2835·6	–
Cobalt	0·2 – 1·0	II 2307·9	15·48
Copper	0·001 – 1·0	I 3274·0	3·78
		I 3247·5	3·82
	1·0 – 1·5	II 2294·4	13·23
		II 2369·9	13·48
		I 2824·4	5·78
		I 2961·2	5·57
Iron	0·002 – 2·2	II 2599·4	12·63
	0·1 – 2·2	I 3020·6	4·11
	0·3 – 3·0	II 2739·5	13·37
		II 2743·2	13·47
		II 2749·2	13·44
		II 2753·3	15·63
		II 2755·7	12·33
		I 2973·2	4·24
		I 2999·5	4·99
Lead	0·1 – 1·0	I 2833·1	4·40

Element	Concentration, %	Wavelength, Å	Excitation energy, eV
1	2	3	4
Magnesium	0·001	II 2802·7	12·06
	0·01 – 3·0	I 2852·1	4·34
		II 2790·8	16·50
		II 2928·8	16·30
		2779·8	–
	9·0 – 16·0	I 2776·7	7·17
		2915·5	–
		I 3332·2	6·43
		I 3329·4	–
Manganese	0·01 – 1·0	II 2593·7	12·20
		2933·1	–
	0·1 – 1·8	II 2949·2	12·80
		II 2672·6	15·77
Nickel	0·02 – 0·5	I 3414·8	3·65
		II 2510·9	14·59
	0·5 – 2·5	II 2416·1	14·61
		I 3101·9	4·42
Silicon	0·002 – 2·0	I 2516·1	4·95
	0·1 – 2·0	I 2881·6	5·08
		I 2528·5	4·93
	2·0 – 11·0	I 2514·3	4·93
		I 2519·2	4·93
	9·0 – 14·0	I 2435·2	5·87
		I 2987·6	4·93
Tin	0·01 – 0·1	I 3175·0	4·33
Titanium	0·01 – 0·25	II 3349·4	10·58
Zinc	0·02 – 0·5	I 3345·0	7·78
	2 – 10	I 3302·6	7·78
		I 3282·3	7·78
		II 2558·0	20·34
		II 2502·0	20·34

are photographed with an ISP-28 (or ISP-22) spectrograph with a three-lens lighting system. The slit-width of the spectrograph is 0·02 mm. The analysis light source is an IG-3 generator. The current is 1·5–2 A, the capacitance 0·005 μF, the inductance 0. The sparking time is 1·5 min. The exposure is 30–60 sec, depending on the type of photographic plate.

The calibration curves for determining silicon, iron, copper, manganese, titanium, zinc and calcium, are given in Fig. 72. The analysis pairs are: Si 2435·2–Al 2652·5 Å; Fe 2749·3–Al 2652·5 Å; Mn 2949·2–Al 2652·5 Å; Cu 3274·0–Al 3050·1 Å; Ti 3234·5–Al 3050·1 Å; Zn 3345·0–Al 3050·1 Å; Ca 3179·3–Al 3050·1 Å.

The basic analysis lines for the analysis of various aluminium-base alloys are given in Table 44.(3, 7)

In view of the difficulty of selecting homologous line pairs in the case of aluminium alloys, great attention should be paid to the maintenance of identical analysis conditions. It is particularly important to keep constant the light-source regime, the analysis-gap length and the shape of the electrodes.

Analysis of aluminium alloys in an a.c. arc is carried out at a current of 2 A.(7) These alloys can also be analysed in a low-voltage (51) and a high-frequency spark.(52)

6. ANALYSIS OF COPPER-BASE ALLOYS

The spectral analysis of copper-base alloys often presents serious difficulties. These alloys contain large amounts of other elements in addition to copper, and "third bodies" interfere with their determination to a large extent. Copper alloys often display substantial non-uniformities of composition (segregation). The spectral analysis of copper-base alloys where the concentrations of the impurities vary between narrow limits, can be carried out by the ordinary methods. In such cases a set of standards should be selected for each grade of alloy. Such alloys can be analysed satisfactorily both in arc and spark light sources.(54)

In the case of many bronzes and brasses, because of the "third body" effects it is impossible to plot the calibration curves under the ordinary analysis conditions. These effects have to be allowed for, (53, 54) or else methods of combating them have to be found. At a number of works a special light source —a low-voltage pulse discharge(55)—is used to eliminate the "third-body" effects.

These effects have been eliminated satisfactorily in the case of spectral analysis by the contact-spark sampling method.(56, 57) The essence of this method is as follows. A capacitor is charged by a d.c. source, and one of the poles of the capacitor is connected to the testpiece while the other is connected to a permanent electrode made of neutral material (Fig. 73). As the electrodes make contact with each other, a spark discharge takes place, as a result of which material of the testpiece is transferred to the permanent electrode. The electrode with the transferred material is then placed in the stand to act as the analysis specimen.

In order to carry out the analysis, samples are taken from the standard and analysis specimens, and burned in an arc or a spark under identical conditions. From the standards a calibration curve is drawn for determining the unknown concentration of the element in the analysis specimen.

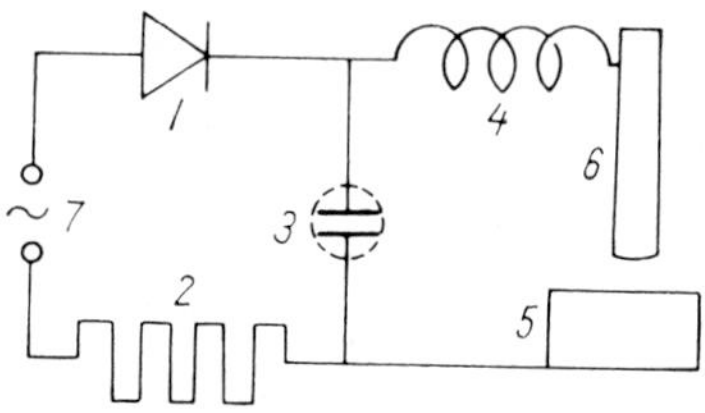

FIG. 73. Electrical diagram of contact-spark sampler.
1—rectifier; *2*—resstor; *3*—capacitor; *4*—inductance; *5*—analysis specimen; *6*—substitute electrode; *7*—a.c. mains.

In the contact-spark sampling method the object is to carry out every alternate single discharge on the freshly-prepared surface of the test-piece. The material for analysis is taken from an area of 2–3 cm^2. Thus the effect of segregation of the alloys on the results of the spectral analysis is reduced.

The material transferred is similar in composition to the analysis specimens. In addition, it is burned-up completely during exposure. Consequently the "third-body" effects are substantially reduced.

As an example we will give the results obtained on analysing some copper-base alloys by the method described.

Samples of standards of tin and phosphor bronzes, and also of silicon and lead brasses, were obtained on a nickel permanent electrode ground hemispherical, as the result of 100 single discharges. The capacitance of the sampler, 80 μF, was charged to 300 V, the self-inductance was about 5 μH.

The sample material was burned with a wedge-shaped carbon substitute electrode, in an a.c. arc at a current of 5 A. The exposure time, sufficient for complete burning-away of the material, was 1 min. The analysis gap was 2 mm. The spectra were photographed with an ISP-28 spectrograph with a three-lens lighting system, using Type I "spectrographic" plates (sensitivity 0·5 GOST units). The slit width of the spectrograph was 0·015 mm. The plates were developed in standard developer. The photometric measurements of the spectrograms were carried out with an MF-2 microphotometer. The calibration curves were plotted by the three-standard method.

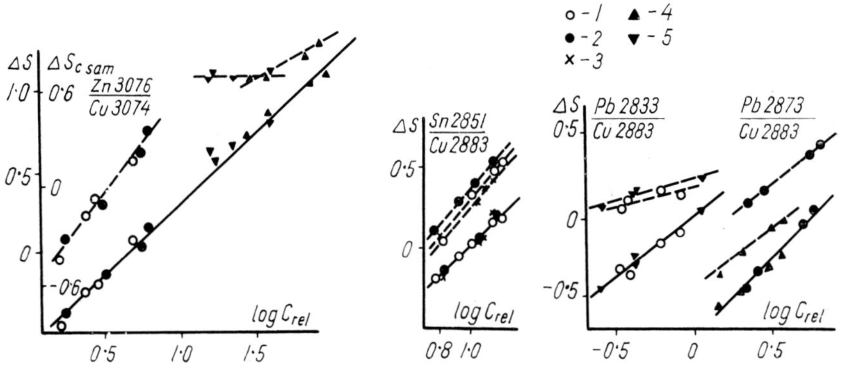

FIG. 74. Calibration curves for determination of zinc, tin and lead in copper-base alloys by means of contact-spark sampling (solid lines) and without sampling (dotted lines).

1—OTsS bronzes; *2*—OTs bronzes; *3*—OF bronzes; *4*—LS bronzes; *5*—LK brasses.

It will be seen from Fig. 74 that in the case of zinc, tin and lead identical calibration curves are obtained for brasses and bronzes, except for the sample of LK brass containing more than 5 per cent of silicon.

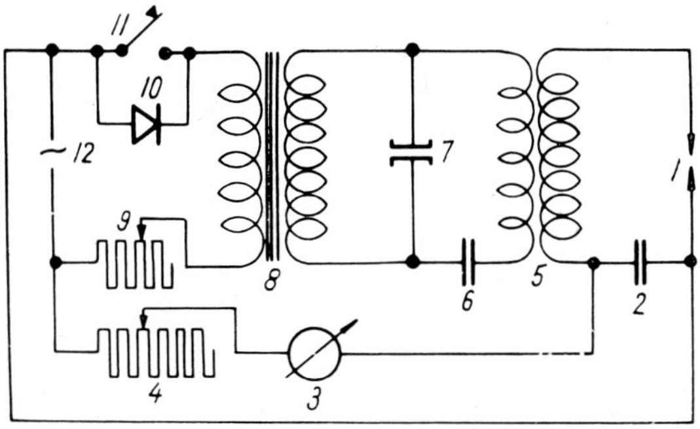

FIG. 75. Electrical diagram of d.c. arc.

1—arc discharge gap; *2*—blocking capacitor; *3*—ammeter; *4*—arc rheostat; *5*—air-cored transformer; *6*—high-frequency circuit capacitor; *7*—discharger; *8*—transformer; *9*—transformer rheostat; *10*—rectifier (DG-Ts24 germanium detectors); *11*—tumbler switch for d.c. or a.c.; *12*—a.c. mains terminals.

The contact-spark sampling method can also be carried out on a.c. In this case the rectifier is removed from the electrical circuit of the sampler (Fig. 73) and the electrolytic capacitors are replaced by paper capacitors of the type

TABLE 45. ANALYSIS SPECTRAL LINES FOR COPPER-BASE ALLOYS

Element	Concentration, %	Wavelength, Å	Excitation energy, eV
1	2	3	4
Aluminium	0·01 – 1·2	I 3082·2	4·02
	0·4 – 1·2	II 2816·2	17·80
	0·5 – 3·5	I 2660·4	4·66
Iron	0·1 – 2·5	II 2755·7	12·33
	0·1 – 7·0	II 2739·5	13·37
	0·1 – 1·5	II 2382·0	13·06
	1·5 – 2·6	II 2749·2	13·44
		II 2753·3	15·63
	3·5 – 7·0	II 2741·4	–
Lead	0·014 – 4·0	I 2833·1	4·40
	0·4 – 4·0	I 2663·2	–
		I 2476·4	–
	2·0 – 9·0	I 2873·3	5·60
Manganese	0·5 – 4·0	II 2949·2	12·80
		2933·1	–
Nickel	2·0 – 6·5	II 2416·1	14·61
		I 3002·5	4·16
		I 3012·0	4·54
		II 2394·5	14·48
		II 2345·3	–
Phosphorus	0·01 – 1·3	I 2554·9	–
		I 2535·6	–
Silicon	0·8 – 1·6	I 2881·6	5·08
	3 – 4	I 2516·1	4·95
		I 2514·3	4·93
Tin	0·15 – 2·5	I 2840·0	4·78
	2 – 12	I 2558·0	–
		I 2706·5	4·78
		I 2850·6	5·41
		I 3009·1	4·33
		I 2863·3	4·32
	5 – 13	I 3175·0	4·33
		I 3262·3	4·87

Element	Concentration, %	Wavelength, Å	Excitation energy, eV
1	2	3	4
Zinc	0·05 – 5·3	I 3302·6	7·78
	0·8 – 32	I 2558·0	20·34
	0·8 – 12·0	I 2801·1	8·50
		I 3345·0	7·78
	2 – 40	I 3075·9	4·03
	4·7 – 53	II 2502·0	20·34

KBG-MN, etc., designed for a.c. with a voltage of not less than 220 V. An arc attachment can also be used for this purpose, if the spark generator is disconnected (p. 13).

The method of carrying out the analysis is the same as in sampling on d.c. The calibration curves for determining zinc, tin and lead in tin bronzes, are given in Fig. 62 (p. 96).

Successful results in the analysis of copper-base alloys have recently been achieved in an arc with constant polarity of the electrodes.[58] When the analysis specimen is used as the cathode the "third-body" effect can be virtually eliminated in tin bronzes and in lead and silicon brasses.

An arc with constant polarity of the electrodes can be obtained by introducing four DG-Ts24 germanium detectors connected in parallel, into the circuit

TABLE 46. COMPARISON LINES OF COPPER USED IN THE ANALYSIS OF COPPER-BASE ALLOYS

Wavelengths, Å	Excitation energy, eV	Wavelengths, Å	Excitation energy, eV
II 2356·6	13·23	II 2721·7	18·65
II 2369·9	13·48	I 2766·4	6·12
II 2400·1	13·42	II 2769·7	18·39
II 2489·6	13·23	I 2824·4	5·78
I 2492·1	4·97	I 2882·9	—
II 2506·3	18·42	I 2961·2	5·57
II 2526·6	—	I 3010·8	5·50
II 2529·3	10·68	I 3036·1	5·72
II 2544·8	18·30	I 3063·4	5·69
II 2590·5	18·65	I 3073·8	5·42
II 2598·8	18·42	I 3308·0	8·82
II 2689·3	18·42	I 3365·4	8·78

of the primary winding of the generator transformer (Fig. 75). The spark under such conditions occurs every half-cycle of the a.c.

The analysis procedure is as follows. The analysis specimens of silicon brasses undergo preliminary heating at a current of 6 A for 2 min. The permanent electrode is wedge-shaped and of copper. The exposure time is 10–40 sec, depending on the sensitivity of the plates. The remaining conditions are

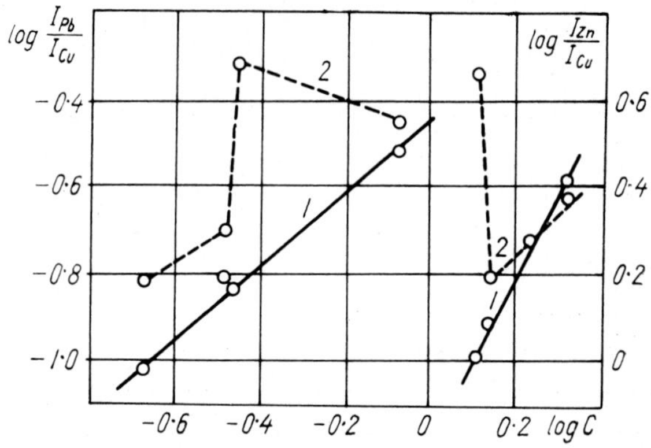

FIG. 76. Calibration curves for determination of lead and zinc in silicon brasses. *1*—in arc with constant polarity of electrodes (specimen—cathode); *2*—in a.c. arc.

the same as in the case of analysis with sampling. Figure 76 shows the calibration curves for the determination of zinc and lead on using an arc of constant polarity. Rectilinear calibration curves are also obtained for the determination of manganese, iron, tin and silicon in silicon brasses.

A large number of elements have to be determined in brasses and bronzes; a list of the analysis lines employed is given in Tables 45 and 46.[3, 6, 7]

CHAPTER V

METHODS OF SPECTRAL ANALYSIS OF POWDERS AND SOLUTIONS

SPECTRAL analysis methods for the analysis of powders and solutions are widely used to study the chemical composition of ores, minerals, slags, soils, glasses, plant ashes, biological material, chemical reagents and the waters of mineral sources. Most of the materials just mentioned occur in the disperse state, while others are converted into this state specially. The need for grinding or dissolving the samples is due to their poor electrical conductivity, the non-uniformity of the distribution of the elements which are being evaluated, and also the great difference in the total composition of the specimens.

Because of some of these factors, monolithic specimens of alloys and metals have to be turned into powder or solution form. The additional operations in the preparaiion of the sample for analysis, are justified by the fact that it thereby becomes possible to eliminate the effect of the structure of the specimens and the non-uniformity of the composition; in some cases it is even possible to reduce the undesirable "third-body" effect. In addition, the problem of obtaining standards is greatly simplified, because large-scale use can then be made of synthetic preparation of the standards.

In the spectral analysis of powders and solutions various methods are used for introducing the sample into the discharge region.

1. INTRODUCTION OF POWDER SAMPLES INTO THE DISCHARGE REGION

Evaporation from a Crater in a Carbon Electrode

With this method the sample is packed into a crater in an electrode of spectrally-pure carbon, and evaporated in a d.c. or a.c. arc. To prevent spraying of the powder, it is fixed in position by organic materials that easily become resinous when heated. Small crystals of cupferron (ammonium nitroso-phenylhydroxylamine) are often used for this purpose. They are placed on the surface of the powder and heated together with the electrode. The powder impregnated with resin is packed tight by means of a glass rod.

Often the sample is covered with a drop of collodion or a layer of salts of the alkali metals. To prevent spraying of the sample, it is also mixed with powdered carbon (1:1 mix), or covered with a layer of powdered carbon.

When the sample is mixed with powdered carbon, the separate particles of the sample are prevented from fusing together into a large drop, and the elements are introduced more uniformly into the discharge region.[(59)] This last-mentioned fact reduced the "third-body" effect.

The material from the crater in the electrode is introduced into the discharge region through evaporation. The rate of introduction of the element will depend basically on its boiling point.

The order in which the material reaches the discharge region is characterized by the series of volatility[(5)] given in Table 47. The elements situated at the start of a series are the most volatile in the series.

The volatility of elements in the free state (series I) corresponds to their boiling points, up to and including iron. The later elements, with a high boiling point, form in addition poorly-volatile compounds with carbon (carbides).

The series of volatility of the oxides (II) does not differ greatly from series I. This is due to the fact that the oxides of many metals decompose in the arc. Processes of decomposition and de-oxidation also take place in the analysis of carbonates and phosphates. Therefore their series of volatility resemble series II.

Sulphides and chlorides are more stable chemical compounds, and they usually evaporate more strongly than do pure metals.

During the initial period of arcing the temperature of the electrode is low, and thus the elements and chemical compounds at the start of the series will evaporate at this point. Lines of such elements as mercury, arsenic, cadmium, zinc, bismuth, sodium, potassium, etc. may appear in the spectrum. As the electrode heats up, elements with a high boiling point will also start to appear strongly.

The temperature of the gas cloud will vary with its composition. In order to obtain uniform discharge conditions throughout the exposure time, the sample is mixed with buffers, which noticeably lower the temperature of the arc and keep it more or less constant during the evaporation of all the samples being studied. Salts of the alkali-metals (NaCl, KCl, Li_2CO_3, etc.) and also ammonium chloride (NH_4Cl) are used as buffers in this way.

The laws governing the introduction of the elements into the discharge region can be determined in specific cases by photographing the spectra on a moving plate (cf. p. 86). These laws can then be used in selecting the required depth of the crater in the carbon electrode, the exposure time, the current and other working conditions.

The materials at the head of the series of volatility, will evaporate from a

TABLE 47. SEQUENCE OF APPEARANCE OF LINES OF SPECTRA OF ELEMENTS IN CARBON ARC

Evaporation of sample from crater in anode

Series I. *Metal alloys*

Hg, As, Cd, Zn, Te, Sb, Bi, Pb, Tl, Mn, Ag, Cu, Sn, Au, In, Ga, Ge, Fe, Ni, Co, V, Cr, Ti, Pt, U, Zr, Hf, Nb, Th, Mo, Re, Ta, W, B.

Series Ia. *Alloys of precious metals*

Ag, Au, Pd, Rh, Pt, Ru, Ir, Os.

Series II. *Oxides*

Hg, As, Cd, Zn, Bi, Sb, B, Pb, Tl, Mo, Sn, W, Mn, Mg, Cu, Ge, In, Ga, Fe, Co Ni, Ba, Sr, Ca, Si, Be, Al, V, Cr, Ti, U, Sc, Mo*, Re*, Zr, Hf, Th, Nb, Ta, W*, B*.

The alkali metals (Li, Na, K, Rb, Cs) lie between zinc and manganese, while the rare-earths (Y, La, Ce, Pr, Nb, Sm, Eu, Gd, Tb, Dy, Ho, Er, Tu, Yb, Lu) lie between chromium and thorium. The elements marked with an asterisk often enter the flame of the arc together with the volatile components of the sample, in the form of easily-evaporating oxides.

Series III. *Carbonates.*

Cd, Zn, (K, Na, Li), Pb, Tl, Mn, Mg, Cu, Fe, Co, Ni, Ba, Sr, Ca.

The elements, the symbols of which appear in brackets, enter the arc flame together.

Series IV. *Phosphates*

(Cd, Zn, Bi, Sn, Pb, Na), (Mn, Mg, Cu), (Fe, Co, Ni), Ca, Al, Cr, (La, Y, Th, Zr).

Series V. *Sulphides*

Hg, As, Ge, Cd, Pb, Sb, Bi, Zn, Tl, Mo, Re, In, Ag, Cu, Ni, Co, Mn, Fe, Mo*, Re*.

Series VI. *Chlorides*

(Li, Na, K, Rb, Cs), Mg, (Ca, Sr, Ba).

Series VII. *Sulphates*

K, Na, Mg, Li, Ca, Ba.

crater 5–8 mm deep. Depending on the size of the sample, the diameter of the crater is taken as 2–4 mm.

In order to improve the sensitivity in determining highly-volatile elements, use is often made of the fact that these elements evaporate at relatively low temperatures. For this purpose a specimen of the sample weighing 50–100 mg is taken, and evaporation is carried out in an arc at a current of 2–5 A. Because of the slow rate of heating of the electrodes at the low current employed, the introduction of the elements of low volatility is retarded. The exposure time should correspond to the time required for the effective introduction of

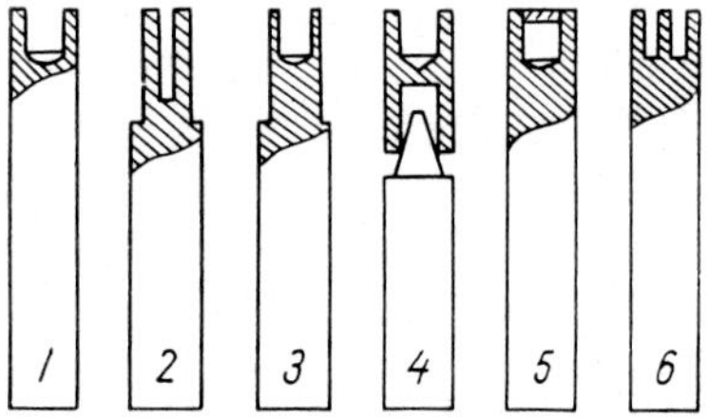

FIG. 77. Usual forms of bottom carbon electrodes.

1—electrode with wide cavity; *2*—electrode with narrow cavity; *4*—electrode with thin cavity walls; *4*—electrode with tip; *5*—electrode with carbon cover (to prevent scattering of sample); *6*—electrode with central projection to reduce straying of discharge.

the impurities being considered, and can be found from spectrograms obtained on a moving plate.

In the determination of poorly-volatile elements the depth of the crater is 2–4 mm, and the current intensity is 10–20 A or sometimes even more. The shape of the carbon electrodes is selected in such a way that the heat loss to the inside is reduced and the heating of the sample is intensified (Fig. 77).

Electrodes heat up differently in a d.c. and in an a.c. arc. In an a.c. arc the temperature at the face of the carbon electrode may reach 2500°. At the cathode of a d.c. arc the temperature is about 3000°, in the region of the anode spot it approaches 4000°. Thus, in order to evaporate poorly-volatile elements it is advisable to have the sample on the anode.[5, 8]

The Use of Moving Electrodes

Sheets of metal or graphite are used as moving electrodes. A track about 1 mm deep and 3–4 mm wide is made along the sheet. The sample is applied in an even layer to the track. The sheet with the sample serves as the bottom electrode, and is placed on a table actuated by an electric motor. A simple design of table is shown in Fig. 78.

With this method a good idea is obtained of the sequence of the introduction of the elements. The moving electrode is most suitable for use in determining the easily-volatile components. But it can also be used successfully to determine the oxides of aluminium, iron, silicon, titanium, magnesium, calcium, etc. The excitation source is an a.c. arc ($I = 10$ A). A spark regime of excitation of the spectrum can also be used.

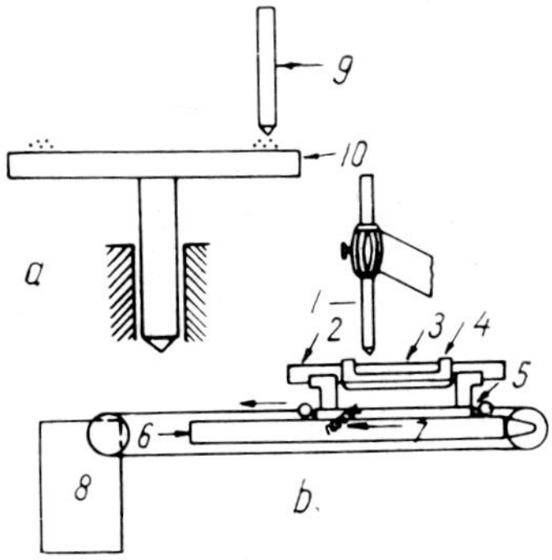

FIG. 78. Diagram of moving bottom electrode: (*a*) rotating electrode; (*b*) table of longitudinal motion.[66]

1—top electrode; *2*—bottom electrode; *3*—plate with sample; *4*—tin clamp; *5*—bed with connectors; *6*—rack; *7*—line connecting rack with bed; *8*—electric drive; *9*—top electrode; *10*—metal (graphite) disc.

Method of Injecting the Sample[(51)]

Essentially this method consists of injecting powder into the arc gap in the form of a fine upward-moving jet. A diagram of the recommended equipment is shown in Fig. 79. The electrodes *1*, of carbon or copper, are arranged horizontally. A given amount of powder is poured into the small vessel *2* of a plastic, which is mounted on the arm of an electric vibrator. As a result of the vibrations the powder settles in the centre, where it is caught in a jet of air and passed through the channel of a fixed pipe *3* into the arc gap. To prevent the jet of powder from deflecting the flame, the position of the latter is stabilized by an additional current of air passing round the small vessel. The current of air deflects the arc flame upwards and holds it in this position. The rate of flow of the air is selected so that the flame does not move out of range of the jet of powder. The air pressure in the pipe connected with the small vessel, is 6–12 cm of water. The diameter of the fixed pipe *3* is 2 mm.

The spectra are excited in an a.c. arc ($I = 8$–10 A). The electrodes remain unsoiled and can be used for long periods without cleaning.

As a result of the continuous exchange of the gas in the arc gap and the reduction of the sequential nature of the evaporation of the powder, this method is a highly sensitive and accurate one. It is in fact an adaptation of the method whereby powder is passed through the analysis gap in the form of a downward-moving jet. The jet of powder issuing from the opening of a conical funnel, is dispersed and the material settles on the electrodes, so that these become covered with the poorly-volatile components. Consequently, the composition of the gas in the discharge region will vary during the exposure

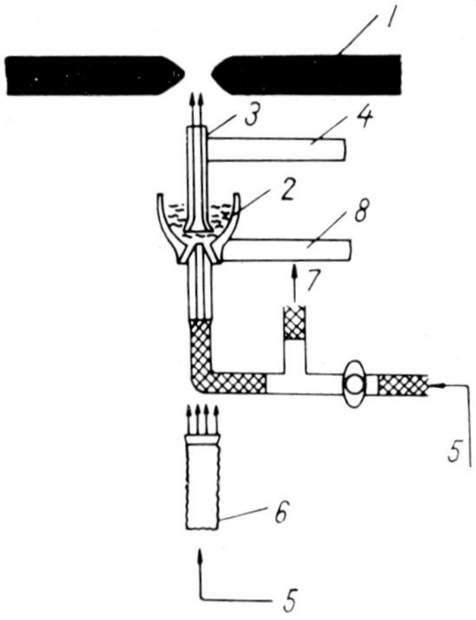

FIG. 79. Diagram of equipment for exciting spectra by the injection method. *1*—electrodes; *2*—vessel of plastic; *3*—pipe for introducing powder into discharge region; *4*—mount; *5*—air supply; *6*—corrugated pipe; *7*—air supply to manometer; *8*—vibrator rod.

time, thus reducing the accuracy of the analysis. In recent years improvements have been proposed to the method of pouring employed, and a special apparatus has been developed for passing the sample into the discharge region (the AVR-2 apparatus).(60) This has slightly reduced the analysis error and made the method of pouring suitable for recommendation for use in production spectral analysis laboratories.

Compaction of Powders

Often the powder being studied is mixed with carbon, copper and other conducting binders, and compacts are made from the mixture thus obtained. Compacts weighing 1–3 g can be made in any press capable of producing pressures of 2000–4000 kg/cm^2. To burn them in an arc (spark), the compacts are placed on a solid metal or carbon electrode.

2. INTRODUCTION OF SOLUTIONS INTO THE DISCHARGE REGION

In the analysis of solutions the sample is a liquid or a salt deposit obtained after evaporation of a small quantity of liquid. Various methods are used to introduce the sample into the discharge region.

Methods of Direct Analysis of Solutions

A revolving disc with different types of flashers is commonly used to supply the solution to the discharge region.

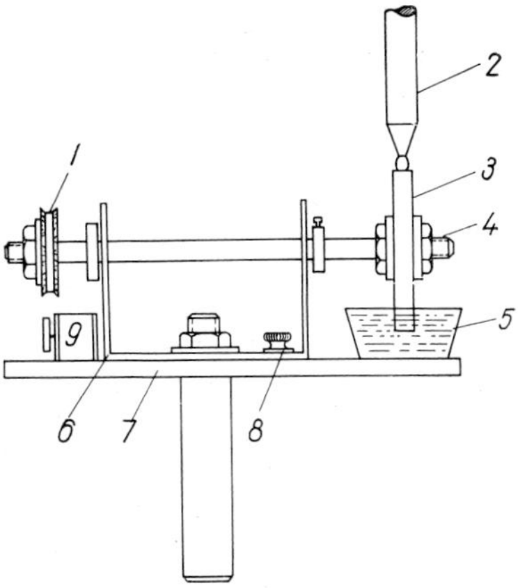

FIG. 80. Diagram of equipment with revolving disc for supplying solution to discharge region.

1—disc; *2*—permanent electrode; *3*—working disc of metal or graphite; *4*—shaft; *5*—container with solution; *6*—metal support; *7*—table of insulating material; *8*—terminal for connexion of lead from arc or spark generator; *9*—Warren motor.

A diagram of typical equipment employing a revolving disc, is shown in Fig. 80. The disc *3*, 4 to 6 cm in diameter, is made of nickel, copper or other neutral and easily-wettable material. It is mounted on the same shaft as disc *1*, which is connected to a Warren motor[(9)] by a Vee-belt. The shaft is fixed to a metal support and is in contact with it. This eliminates the need for a special sliding contact. The whole system is mounted on a table of insulating material. The table is fitted into the bottom holder of a type PS-162 support, the top holder of which carries the permanent electrode. The use of the standard support facilitates the setting and control of the electrodes.

The bottom of the working disc is immersed in the solution. The surface of the disc wetted with solution is rotated at a uniform rate (say 3–4 rev/min).

The excitation source of the spectrum may be an arc or a spark. Before photographing the spectrum, heating should be carried out for a time equal to one complete revolution of the disc.

Figure 81 illustrates a simple type of flasher. The small vessel *1* of the flasher 2–3 cm in diameter, can be made of molybdenum glass. In the bottom of the small vessel there is an opening into which a graphite (or copper) rod *3* fits tightly. By means of this rod the flasher is fixed to the holder of the support.

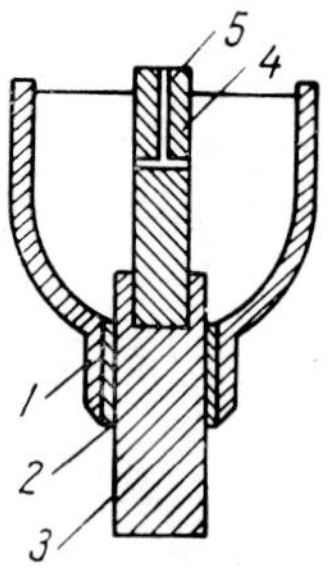

FIG. 81. Diagram of flasher.

1—vessel of molybdenum glass; *2*—rubber insert; *3*—graphite holder of carbon electrode; *4*—electrode; *5*—capillary.

A carbon electrode containing a capillary 0·8–1·0 mm in diameter is inserted in a cradle in the graphite rod. The solution enters the capillary via the side branches of the electrode, and then the liquid rises through capillary forces until a thin layer of it wets the face of the electrode. When the arc (spark) is switched on, the sample evaporates directly from this thin layer of liquid.

Methods of Analysing Salt Deposits

About 0·2–0·3 ml. of solution is introduced into the crater in a carbon electrode. The salts formed after the analysis solution has evaporated, are burned in an arc. To prevent the solution from penetrating deep into the electrode, the crater in the latter is impregnated with kerosene or a 5 per cent solution of polystyrene in benzene.

It is also possible to immerse carbon rods 8–10 mm long in the analysis solution for 1–2 hr. These rods are then dried and used as analysis specimens. Of course, with this method of introducing the material it is difficult to evaporate it completely.

This drawback can be eliminated by dropping the solution on to the end of a carbon electrode which has been impregnated beforehand with one to two drops of a 5 per cent solution of polystyrene in benzene. The resulting film of polystyrene will then break down slightly under the action of a weak (5 per cent) solution of sulphuric acid. The sulphuric acid can be introduced into the analysis solution, or else it can be applied to the electrode separately. The solution will partially penetrate into the carbon through the broken film of polystyrene. The salts will concentrate in a thin surface layer, and they can be evaporated completely in an arc or a spark. Through the correct execution of these simple operations the sensitivity of the determination of many elements can be improved severalfold.[61]

A high analysis sensitivity can also be achieved using Feldman's method,[62] the essentials of which are as follows. The solution is poured into a small cylindrical hole drilled into a carbon rod. The cylinder is connected by the top electrode. The solution soaks through the thin porous bottom of the cylinder and evaporates into the discharge region. The light source is a high-voltage spark; it is difficult to use an arc, because the solution boils away rapidly. The method described is used at the Minsk Medical Institute to determine microscopic amounts of elements in biological materials.[63]

3. OBTAINING STANDARDS AND PREPARING SPECIMENS FOR ANALYSIS

The conditions regarding the standards of alloys (p. 111) also apply to the standards of powders and solutions, as well as the following conditions:

(1) the particles of the powders of the standards should be the same size as the particles of the analysis sample;

(2) the elements being determined should be present in the standards in the form of the same chemical compounds as in the samples;

(3) in the analysis of solutions the same solvent should be used in the standards as in the analysis samples;

(4) the standards for the determination of small concentrations of elements should be made with allowances for the purity of the reagents employed.

The powder standards can easily be obtained if a monotypic sample which has been analysed accurately by chemical methods is available. This sample is then taken as the basic standard. By thinning the material of this standard with "pure base" we can obtain two to three standards containing smaller concentrations of the elements being evaluated. By "pure base" we mean a given element or chemical compound thereof, which is present in the analysis samples in large proportions (80–90 per cent).

Often a mixture of several elements of known composition has to be taken as the base. In such cases, which are the rule rather than the exception, the pure base is a monotypic sample which does not contain the elements being evaluated.

To make standards of high concentrations, additions of the components being evaluated are made to the initial sample. We will consider this case with reference to the calculation of the concentrations in standards designed for the analysis of peat ash with respect to its content of oxides of silicon, magnesium and aluminium. The concentrations of the components being evaluated may vary within the following limits: SiO_2 5–55 per cent, AL_2O_3 4–18 per cent, MgO 3–16 per cent. In order to cover the range of variation in the concentrations in the samples, four to five standards are required, the content of the component in question rising by a factor of 1·5–2 in each succeeding standard. The possible concentrations of the oxides in the standards are given in Table 48.

TABLE 48

Standard No.	Content of oxides being evaluated, %		
	SiO_2	Al_2O_3	MgO
1	4	20	12
2	8	15	8
3	16	9	20
4	32	6	4
5	60	3	2

Let us suppose that a sample containing 6 per cent of SiO_2, 0·5 per cent of MgO and 2 per cent of Al_2O_3 was obtained as the base. The other concentrated components are oxides (or salts) of calcium, sodium and iron. The majority of the material of this sample is CaO (about 70 per cent). It is proposed to prepare 10 g of powder of each standard. The concentration of SiO_2 in the first standard is 4 per cent, and in the sample 6 per cent. With respect to 10 g of powder we should take (4:6)·10 g = 6·67 g of the initial sample. This amount of the initial sample will contain 0·133 g of Al_2O_3 (2 per cent of 6·67 g). On the basis of the selected conditions, 2·0 g of Al_2O_3 (20 per cent of 10 g) should be introduced. Thus, the addition of this oxide should be 2·0–0·133 g = = 1·867 g. The amount of MgO to be added to the first standard, can be calculated in a similar way. We find that this equals 1·167 g. The sum of the ash of the initial standard and of the additions of Al_2O_3 and MgO is 9·7 g. This mixture is then made up to 10 g with the oxide CaO.

The additions to the other standards can be calculated more easily, because here the concentrations of the oxides being evaluated are larger than in the initial sample. The quantity of oxide to be added P_i can be calculated from the following equation:

$$\Delta P_i = \frac{P}{100}\left((C_i - C_{0i})\frac{100-\sum C_i}{100-\sum C_{0i}}\right),$$

where P is the weight of the standard, C_{0_i} and C_i are the concentrations of the element in question in the initial sample and in the standard, respectively, $\sum C_{0i}$ is the sum of the concentrations of all the oxides being evaluated, in the initial sample, $\sum C_i$ is the similar sum for the standard being produced. The subscript i replaces the symbol of the chemical element or compound.

When it is necessary to calculate the content of the element in its chemical compound the factor M/nA should be introduced into the equation; here M

is the molecular weight of the given compound; A is the atomic weight of the element being determined, and n is the number of atoms of this element per molecule of the chemical compound.

The additions of all the components being evaluated, can be calculated in succession from the above equation. The required size of the initial sample is found from the difference in the weights of the standard and the sum of the additions.

An internal standard should be introduced into all the standards. For example, in the case being considered copper oxide CuO can be taken, adding it in amounts totalling 50 per cent of the weight of the standard. The internal standard is added to all the analysis samples in the same proportion. The standards and the samples are thinned with sodium salt (NaCl) and graphite powder in the ratio 1:2:2.

By means of intensive thinning it is possible to reduce the analysis errors due to the difference in the compositions of the samples being studied. Moreover, sodium stabilizes the temperature of the arc. The role of the graphite powder is to eliminate the formation of a large drop and to reduce the sequential nature of the introduction of the analysis material.

If no initial sample of accurately determined composition is available, a pure base of the sample has to be prepared, by mixing the required chemically-pure compounds (oxides, sulphides, sulphates, carbonates, etc.) in the correct proportions. Chemical compounds of the elements being evaluated, are added to the quantity of base prepared. Calculation is carried out according to the equation given above, assuming that $C_0 = 0$. It is advisable to make the standard corresponding to the upper concentration limits expected in the samples, first. Then the other standards can be made by thinning the quantity of standard obtained, with powder of the base.

Before being mixed, the powder of the base and the compounds being introduced, should be carefully ground in an agate mortar and passed through a sieve (150 to 200 mesh). After making the standards, the powder should be mixed carefully by shaking them up for a long time. This process can be considerably speeded up by using a special mixer.[60] The mixer consists of a table to which the containers with the powder inside them are securely fixed. The table is moved backwards and forwards by an electric motor, and as a result of the frequent and violent shaking a uniform mixture of powder is obtained in a few minutes.

The standards for the analysis of solutions are prepared by dissolving salts or pure metals in a suitable solvent. The salts selected should not form deposits on being dissolved together. When the standard is thinned substantially, the presence of impurities in chemically-pure reagents is unimportant; they need be taken into account only in determining small concentrations (10^{-2} to 10^{-5} per cent).

Initial solutions are prepared beforehand for each element being evaluated. For this the required weight of salts or metals is weighed out on an analytical balance, and then dissolved in 200–400 ml. of solvent. It is advisable to use even larger volumes of liquid than this. In this way the permissible error in proportioning the solutions can be reduced.

Metals will readily dissolve in *aqua regia* (three parts of HCl to one of HNO_3). To accelerate dissolution, the solution should be boiled. In making standards from salts the latter should be dissolved in a 30–50 per cent aqueous solution of the acids used to dissolve the analysis samples.

The concentrations of the elements being evaluated in the initial solutions should be three to five times the concentration in the standards. Chemical analysis of the initial solutions is carried out if salts containing substantial amounts of impurities are used, and the number of water molecules making up their chemical composition is unknown. When the composition of the salts is known, the sum of the impurities in the weighed portion can be allowed for, and it is then unnecessary to carry out a chemical control of the initial solutions. The concentration of the initial solutions obtained by dissolving turnings of pure metals, depends on the size of the weighed portion employed.

The standards are prepared by mixing the initial solutions in given proportions. The concentration of each element in the standards depends on its weight expressed as a percentage of the total weight of the metals in solution. If the element is present in the sample as a chemical compound, then it should be introduced into the standard in the same compound. In this case the concentration of the element in the standards equals the ratio between its weight and the weight of all the dissolved materials. If an internal standard is used, then it should be added to the solvent beforehand. The concentration of the internal standard is taken as about several per cent. Also 20–30 per cent of sodium salts should be introduced into the solvent, to stabilize the discharge temperature during the process of excitation of the analysis material.

The samples for analysis should be prepared with the same care as the standards. The powder standard is ground, passed through a sieve, and the weighed portion thereof is mixed with the internal standard. The raw material of the sample is dried beforehand in a drying cupboard at a temperature of 100–120°. The same solvent is used to dissolve the sample as was used for the standards, together with the same internal standard and buffer.

4. ADDITION METHOD

The addition method enables the content of impurities in the analysis sample to be determined without recourse to chemical analysis during the process of preparation of the standards. This method is used mostly in the determination of very small concentrations of elements (10^{-3} to 10^{-6} per cent). In such cases chemical analysis gives a large error and cannot be used to study the composition of the materials employed in making the standards.

With the addition method the standards are made on the basis of the sample being studied, as follows: three to four identical weighed portions of the sample being studied are taken, and various additions of the elements being evaluated are added to them. The first addition should be more or less equal to the content of the impurity in the sample being investigated. The additions to the succeeding portions should be two to three times greater each time. Let us call these additions C_1, C_2, C_3. Where necessary an internal standard is introduced into the inital sample and the samples containing additions. Then these samples are photographed under uniform conditions. The relative intensity of the analysis line pair can be found from the spectrograms obtained —it is connected with the concentration C in the specimens by the following relation:

$$\frac{I}{I_0} = AC^b.$$

The coefficient $b \leqslant 1$. It determines the self-absorption of the lines in the discharge region. In the case of small concentrations of the impurity the absorption of its lines is low, i.e. it can be assumed that $b = 1$[(3)] The relative intensity will be directly proportional to the content of the element in the specimen:

$$\frac{I}{I_0} = AC.$$

This relation gives a straight line when it is represented graphically. We plot the size of the additions along the abscissae, and the corresponding intensity of the analysis pair along the ordinates. The calibration straight line (Fig. 82) cuts off along the ordinate axis ($C=0$) the section OA corresponding to the intensity of the analysis pair of the sample being studied. The impurity concentration in the latter depends on the size of the section cut off by the calibration straight line along the abscissae ($OB = x$).

It is advisable to repeat the analysis and the determination of the concentration x. Then the initial sample and the samples with additions can be used to plot the graph by the three-standard method. The impurity concentration in the standards will be: x per cent, $(x+C_1)$ per cent, $(x+C_2)$ per cent, $(x+C_3)$ per cent, etc.

In the variant of the addition method being considered it was assumed that $b = 1$. But in practice it is found that even at low concentrations substantial self-absorption takes place of the lines of the impurity being evaluated $(b < 1)$. In such cases the use of the linear interpolation method valid for $b = 1$, will lead to substantial errors. Thus the successive approximation method has to be used.[64, 65]

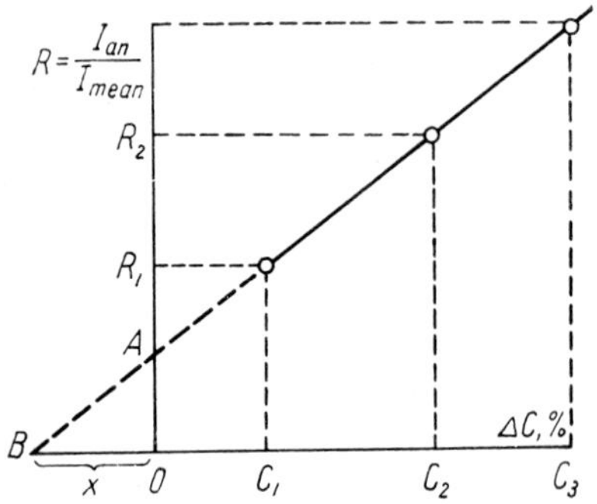

FIG. 82. Calibration straight line for determining content of impurity in sample by addition method ($b = 1$). Sizes of additions plotted along abscissae, relative intensity of analysis pair along ordinates.

One of the variants of this method[66] enables the impurity concentration in the initial sample to be calculated according to the equation:

$$x = \frac{a}{c-2a},$$

where a and c are the sizes of the additions made to uniform weighed portions of the sample, and $2a < c$. This equation is obtained on condition that in the case of the weighed portion with addition a the difference between the degrees of blackening of the analysis line pair equals the arithmetic mean of the differences between the degrees of blackening of the portion with addition c and of the initial sample with the concentration of the element being evaluated x.

In practice we proceed as follows. A curve is plotted within the coordinates: size of addition and difference in degrees of blackening of analysis pair,*

* If there is a substantial continuous background, it should be allowed for on the basis of the rules given on p. 108.

on the basis of the spectra of the sample and the spectra of three to four specimens with additions. Knowing ΔS_x for the initial sample and ΔS_{x+c} for the specimen with the larger addition, we can find the arithmetic mean of these quantities:

$$\frac{\Delta S_x + \Delta S_{x+c}}{2} = \Delta S_{x+a}$$

On the calibration curve we read off the size of the addition a corresponding to ΔS_{x+a}. Inserting the value of a and also the size of the larger addition c into the equation, we can calculate the concentration in the initial sample.

The method described above places no restrictions on b. It is also valid in cases where b is not equal to unity and the slope of the curve differs from 45°.

In determining small concentrations care should be taken to avoid soiling of the material by the vessels, reagents, etc. The acids used as solvents should not contain the impurities being evaluated. The water used in the solution and to rinse the vessels, should be doubly distilled.

5. SEMI-QUANTITATIVE SPECTROGRAPHIC ANALYSIS

Semi-quantitative spectrographic analysis is used to estimate the contents of elements in materials of complex chemical composition. The relative error of this method is 15–40 per cent.

Some advantages of semi-quantitative analysis are its speed and simplicity. Contrary to the rough quantitative determinations using a spectroscope, by semi-quantitative spectrographic analysis on the basis of a single spectrogram it is possible to estimate the concentrations of a large number of elements present in a sample. Under works conditions it can be used at an early stage in the development of procedures for the quantitative analysis of slags, glasses, soils, lubricating oils, building materials, various production wastes, etc. In the analysis of certain of these materials it may be the only method of checking their chemical composition.

Semi-quantitative spectral analysis is used a very great deal in geological surveying, to study the distribution of the elements in the earth's crust. For this purpose it often suffices to classify specimens in which the contents of the elements being considered differ by a factor of 3 or 4: i.e. 0·001%, 0·003%, 0·01%, 0·03%, 0·1%, etc.

There are various semi-quantitative analysis methods, all of which are based on the comparison of the spectra of samples and of standards obtained on one or more photographic plates. The quantity of the sample, the conditions under which it is evaporated and excited, should be kept constant.

Semi-quantitative analysis is generally based on the degrees of blackening of the spectral lines. The analysis standards do not contain an internal standard.

By observing in a spectrum projector spectra of standards and samples that have been photographed together, it is possible to compare therein the degrees of blackening of the lines of the elements being considered. When the intensities of the selected impurity lines in the spectra of one of the standards and of the sample, are equal to each other, this indicates that they contain equal amounts of the impurity in question. If no absolute equality is found, then an approximate estimate is made between the two standards where the impurity line is next darkest and next lightest respectively in comparison with the blackening in the spectrum of the sample.

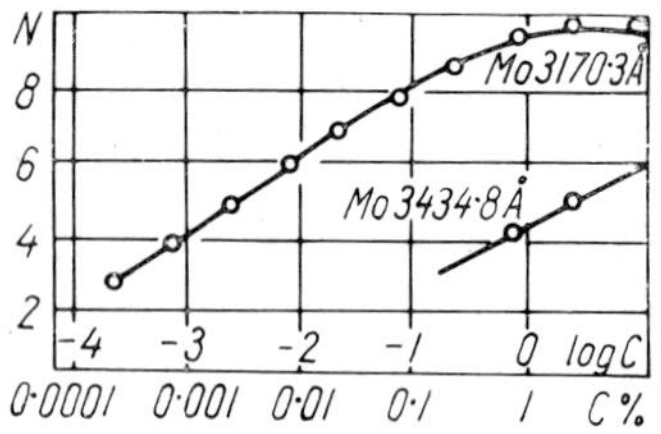

FIG. 83. Calibration curves for approximate quantitative evaluation of molybdenum.[67] Concentrations in logarithmic scale plotted along abscissae, and number of steps of absorber (N) along ordinates.

The number of lines of an element in the spectrum depends on the concentration of the element in the sample. This makes it possible to find out beforehand from the spectra of the standards which lines of the element in question will appear at a given concentration. The contents in the specimens being studied can then be estimated on the basis of these criteria.

The most rational method is that proposed in Ref. 67, of photographing the spectra of the specimens and standards through a ten-step absorber. The spectra can be observed best in a spectrum projector.

For each element sensitive lines free from superimpositions are selected (Table 2, p. 25). The greater the concentration of the element, the greater is the number of steps of the absorber in which its lines will appear.

From the spectra of the standards nomograms can be devised, which indicate the length of the analysis of a given elements at different concentrations in the standards. Then the concentrations in the samples of the elements being considered can be found by comparing these nomograms with the length of the lines in the spectra of the samples.

Calibration curves (Fig. 83) can be used instead of nomograms. These curves are drawn by plotting the logarithm of the concentration of the element in the standard against the number of steps of the absorber in which the analysis line of the element appears.

The semi-quantitative determination of most elements is carried out on the basis of spectrograms obtained with an ISP-28 (ISP-22) spectrograph. The sample is usually introduced into the discharge region from a channel in a carbon electrode. To stabilize the arc temperatures the sample should be mixed with a buffer.

A method of this type is described in Ref. 68. The sample and standard materials are thinned by a buffer mixture of graphite and soda (graphite 50 per cent, remainder soda and sample) The powder is packed tightly into the crater (diameter 2 mm, depth 5 mm) of a carbon electrode 6 mm in diameter. A drop of soda solution is placed on top of the sample; in order to release into the arc the surplus of sodium atoms it is recommended that the bottom electrode be wrapped in gauze wetted with concentrated soda solution.

The spectra is excited in an a.c. arc, current 7 A, analysis gap length 3 mm. The spectra are photographed with an ISP-22 (ISP-28) spectrograph through a standard eight-step absorber. The width of the spectrograph slit is 0·008 mm, the lighting system is a standard three-lens system. Diapositive plates (sensitivity 0·25 GOST units) are used. The exposure time is 6 min. The concentrations of the elements are determined using Kler's method.(67)

With the method described it is possible to determine Al, Ba, Be, V, Fe, Ca, Si, Mg, Cu, Ag, Sr, Ti, Cr to a sensitivity of within 0·0001 per cent; Bi, W, Ga, Mo, Ni, Sn, Zr, In to within 0·001 per cent; Co, Li, Mn, Pb, Tl, Ge to within hundredths of 1 per cent; Cd, Sb, Zn to within tenths of 1 per cent; As, P, Te to about 1 per cent.

6. QUANTITATIVE SPECTROGRAPHIC ANALYSIS OF SLAGS

The methods of analysing slags can be classified on the basis of the way in which the sample is introduced into the discharge region. They consist either of supplying of finely-ground sample, or compacting the slag, or turning it into a solution. In the first two cases the composition of the sample greatly affects the results of the analysis. This is primarily due to the sucessive nature of the introduction of the sample, and the differences in the chemical compounds in which the constituent elements occur. The volatility and the strength of the molecules of these compounds differ, hence the rate at which they are introduced into the discharge region will also differ, and the relationship between the line intensities and the concentration of the element in the sample will vary.

On analysing slag in powder form a further error may arise due to unsatisfactory mixing of the sample. The effects of the factors listed above can be greatly reduced by turning the slag into a solution. The accuracy of the analysis of slags from solutions is greater, but this method also takes slightly longer, so that in many cases the use of powder slag analysis methods is justified.

The moving-electrode method (69, 70) is used to analyse chromium and vanadium slags. With this method 0·3–0·5 g of powder ground to a fineness of 200 mesh, is applied in a strip 10–12 mm wide and 80–90 mm long to a metal sheet, which travels at a rate of 1 mm/sec during exposure. The top electrode is of the same material as the sheet (copper or nickel) and is wedge-shaped with a working area 3–3·5 mm in diameter. The length of the analysis gap is 2–3 mm. The spectra are excited in an a.c. arc (I = 11–12 A) and an ISP-22 (ISP-28) instrument with a three-lens system is used for photographing them. The aperture in the iris diaphragm is 1·2 mm. The width of the spectrograph slit is 0·01 mm. Diapositive plates (sensitivity 0·25–0·5 GOST units) can be used. The exposure time is 1·5–2 min. In this time 70–80 per cent of the sample can be burned-up.

The line intensity is measured by means of visual photometry, which considerably speeds up the treatment of the spectrograms. Lines of the electrode material are used as the standard lines. The curves are plotted within the coordinates log (I_x/I_0), log C.

TABLE 49. RANGE OF CONCENTRATIONS OF COMPOUNDS BEING EVALUATED, AND ANALYSIS LINE PAIRS FOR THE ANALYSIS OF LOW-CHROMIUM ORES

Compound being evaluated	Range of concentrations, %	Wavelengths of analysis line pairs, Å
CaO	30·0 – 50·0	Ca 3158·9 – Cu 3142·4
Cr_2O_3	1·0 – 10·0	Cr 2865·1 – Cu 2882·9
FeO_{total}	2·0 – 15·0	Fe 3075·7 – Cu 3073·8
SiO_2	6·0 – 25·0	Si 2881·6 – Cu 2824·4
Al_2O_3	3·0 – 20·0	Al 3082·2 – Cu 3073·8
MgO	5·0 – 13·0	Mg 2802·7 – Cu 2824·4
MnO	2·0 – 10·0	Mn 2933·1 – Cu 2882·9

Table 49 gives the wavelengths of the spectral lines selected for the analysis of low-chromium slags, and the range of concentrations of the compounds being evaluated. The error of this method is 1·5–5 per cent of the content. Analysis of seven elements in a specimen can be carried out in 25 min. The moving plate and the top electrode are made of pure copper.

In the analysis of high-chromium and vanadium slags the permanent electrode and the bottom moving-sheet electrode are made of nickel. The conditions of excitation and photography are as before. The components Cr_2O_3, FeO_{total}, SiO_2, CaO, MgO and Al_2O_3 have been evaluated in high-chromium slags. The following line pairs were selected for visual photometry: Cr 3125·0–Ni 3114·1 Å, Fe 3047·6–Ni 3045·0 Å; Si 2881·6–Ni 2821·3 Å; Ca 3179·3–Ni 3145·7 Å; Mg 2783·0–Ni 2805·1 Å; Al 3082·2–Ni 3080·8 Å.

In the case of vanadium slags iron is determined from the line pair Fe 3083·7–Ni 3099·1 Å, and vanadium from the line pair V 3110·7–Ni 3114·1 Å. Calcium, silicon, aluminium and magnesium are determined from the line pairs used in the case of high-chromium slags.

The moving electrode method using an a.c. arc is characterized by highly selective introduction of the individual components into the discharge region. This method can be used only in cases where the samples are of equal composition. Separate standards corresponding in composition to the samples, are required when slags of different grades have to be analysed.[(72)]

Blast furnace slags and sinters are usually analysed in compact or solution form.[(73–78)] The compacts are normally of the following composition: 0·1 g of slag, 2 g of spectrally-pure graphite powder. Oxides of chromium or molybdenum (titanium) are added as comparison elements to the mix, in amounts totalling 0·1–0·3 g. The fineness of grinding of the powder is 200 mesh. The mix should be well-mixed, and pressed into compacts 12 mm in diameter at a pressure of 3000 kg/cm^2.

The optimum conditions for excitation of the spectrum are as follows: IG-2 spark generator (complex connexion), voltage in primary circuit 220 V, capacitance of discharge circuit 0.01 μF, self inductance 0·05–0·15 mH, current strength 1·4–1·6 A (one discharge per half-cycle of the current). The permanent electrode is a wedge-shaped carbon rod 6 mm in diameter. The spectra are photographed with an ISP-28 (ISP-22) spectrograph, slit width 0·015 mm. The analysis line pairs used are given in Table 50.

The arithmetic mean error is 2–5 per cent.

The "third-body" effect is not found with these methods. This is due first to the extensive thinning of the sample by graphite powder, and second to the less selective introduction of the material into the spark-discharge region compared with an a.c. arc.

In the case of analysis from solutions,[(78)] powdered slag in amounts of 0·5–0·3 g is mixed with "plaven" flux (two parts of soda to three of borax) in the ratio 1:5. The mix thus obtained is placed in a platinum crucible and sintered for 2–3 min in a muffle furnace at a temperature of 900–1000°C. Then the cooled crucible together with the sintered mix is lowered into a container containing 75 ml. of hot nitric acid diluted in the ratio 1:3. The container is covered with glass and the contents are boiled for 2 min to dissolve the sample completely. The solution obtained is made up to 250 ml. with distilled water.

It is recommended that solutions of chromium or molybdenum be used as internal standards. Aqueous solutions of chromium (concentration 75 per cent) and molybdenum can be produced by dissolving potassium dichromate or

TABLE 50. RANGE OF CONCENTRATIONS OF COMPOUNDS BEING EVALUATED, AND ANALYSIS LINE PAIRS FOR ANALYSIS OF SLAGS IN COMPACTS AND SOLUTIONS

Compound being evaluated	Range of concentrations, %	Lines of element being evaluated, Å	Wavelengths of standard lines, Å		
			Cr	Mo	Ti
CaO	17–58	Ca 3158·9	3147·2	3152·8	3194·8
SiO_2	6–25	Si 2516·1	2571·7	—	—
		Si 2881·8	—	2872·9	2956·1
Al_2O_3	2–13	Al 3092·7	3053·9	3077·7	3101·5
MgO	2–12	Mg 2790·8	2789·4	2779·2	—
		Mg 2852·1	—	2863·8	2948·3
MnO	2–25	Mn 2939·3	2941·9	—	2938·7
		Mn 2933·1	—	2934·3	—
FeO_{total}	6–30	Fe 2755·7	2756·3	—	2764·8

ammonium molybdate in distilled water. The concentration of the molybdenum in the solution should be 3·5 per cent.

Before carrying out the analysis, the slag solution is mixed with the chromium solution in the ratio 2:1 or with the molybdenum solution in the ratio 70:1.

The solution is introduced into the discharge gap by means of a flasher (Fig. 81) or a copper revolving disc (Fig. 80). In the first case the bottom electrode is a carbon rod ($d = 6$ mm, $h = 10$ mm) that has undergone preliminary heating at 900° for 3 min. The electrode is fixed into the holder of the flasher and projects 1 mm above the solution. The spark generator regime is the same as that used to analyse compacts.

An ISP-28 (ISP-22) spectrograph is used, slit width 0·015 mm. The slit is illuminated by a spherical condenser placed at the standard distance indicated in the instructions supplied with the spectrograph.

The analysis line pairs used, are given in Table 50.

The error of the individual determinations of CaO and SiO_2 is 2–3 per cent, while for Al_2O_3, MgO and MnO it is 3–5 per cent.

CHAPTER VI

SETTING UP A SPECTRAL ANALYSIS LABORATORY

In setting up a spectral analysis laboratory at a works it is advisable to start by buying apparatus for visual analysis. Above all it is necessary to acquire an SL-11 (or SL-13) spectroscope. In order to undertake photographic methods of spectral analysis a separate room should be provided and an ISP-28 spectrograph, a PS-18 (or SPP-1) spectrum projector and an MF-2 microphotometer should be bought. The cost of the entire apparatus is 35–40 thousand roubles and can be recovered in one to two years.

Later, when the number of analyses has to be greatly increased, a spectral analysis laboratory can be set up. To do this suitable accomodation, instruments, materials and also trained teams of technicians and laboratory assistants are required. Standard designs have been drawn up for large, medium-size and small spectral analysis laboratories or control points, depending on the nature and the volume of the spectral analysis work to be carried out. At institutes and central laboratories of very large undertakings where in addition to routine analyses considerable scientific research work has to be carried out, a large spectral analysis laboratory is required. At institutes where the volume of research work is smaller, and at works where the routine analyses do not total more than several hundred per day, a medium-size spectral analysis laboratory will suffice. At works where the volume of analysis work is much smaller, a small spectral analysis laboratory will suffice. Such a laboratory can also be provided for rapid analysis purposes in casting, open-hearth and steel-melting bays. Spectroscope or spectrometer control points are set up at works in the shops, the stores or the stock yards.

1. Buildings and Fittings of Spectral Analysis Laboratories

The building for a spectral analysis laboratory should be located close to the areas it is designed to serve, on ground or first-floor level, some distance from any machinery and apparatus where vibrations are set up, and should be sufficiently large for all the apparatus and instruments to be arranged satisfactorily. All laboratories and control points should be housed in dry (relative humidity not more than 75 per cent) and heated buildings equipped with natural and artificial lighting, water supply, mains drainage, ventilation and exhaust fans, electric power and earthing installations.

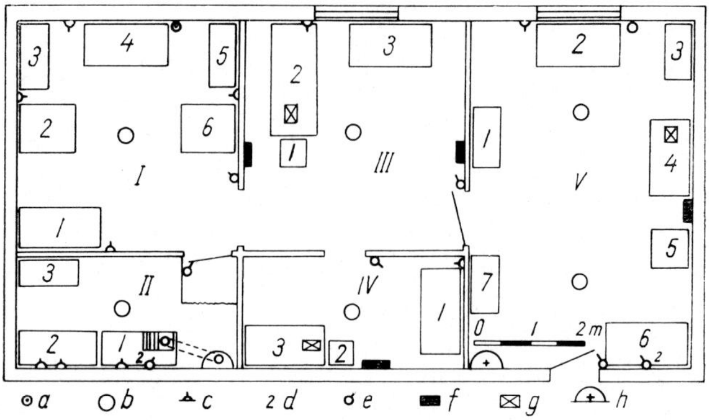

FIG. 84. Plan and arrangement of equipment of a small spectral analysis laboratory.

a—telephone; *b*—light fitting; *c*—power outlet, ~ 127 or 220 V, 6 A; *d*—single-socket wall bracket; *e*—6-A switch; *f*—laboratory board with terminals and sockets, ~ 127 V and ~ 220 V, 20 A; *g*—individual ventilation; *h*—basin.

I. Photometer room:

1—work table; *2*—MF-2 microphotometer; *3*—book case; *4*—writing table; *5*—instrument cabinet; *6*—PS-18 spectrum projector.

II. Photography room:

1—developing table with pan; *2*—photographic work table; *3*—cabinet for photographic plates and chemicals.

III. Spectrograph room:

1—I.G-3 generator; *2*—ISP-28 spectrograph; *3*— work table.

IV. Spectrometer room:

1—work table; *2*—IG-3 generator; *3*—ST-7 spectrometer.

V. Sample preparation room:

1—cupboard for analysed samples; *2*—work table; *3*—cupboard for standards; *4*—table for spectroscope; *5*—emery wheel; *6*—work bench; *7*—cloaks cupboard.

The air temperature in the building should not vary beyond the limits 18–25°C. Spectral analysis work cannot be carried out in rooms where chemical analysis work is performed, because acid and alkali vapours will rapidly damage the valuable instruments.

The walls and ceilings of the rooms should be painted with light-coloured oil paints. The floors in all the buildings should be of wood covered with lino. The windows should all be fitted with dark blinds which can be handled easily. The south-facing windows should also be provided with lightweight thin blinds. Individual lighting should be provided for all the spectral analysis installations.

In planning the laboratory separate rooms should be provided for preparing the samples, photographing the spectra, for the spectrometer, for treating the photographic materials, and for photometer work. The number of rooms will depend on the type of laboratory. A small spectral analysis laboratory (Fig. 84) will contain: a room for preparing the samples (24 m^2), a spectro-

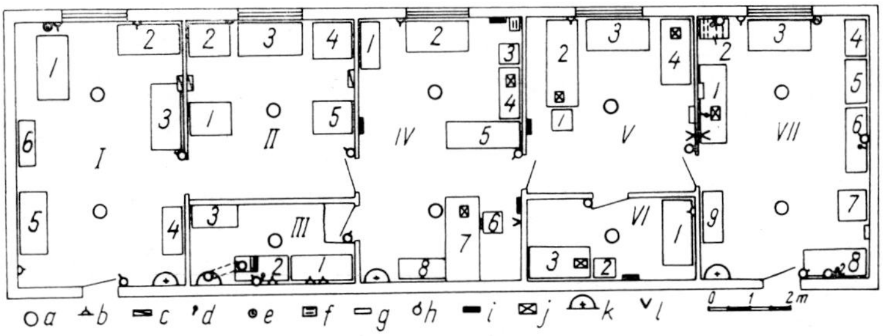

FIG. 85. Plan and arrangement of equipment of a medium-size spectral analysis laboratory.

a—light fitting; *b*—power outlet, ~ 127 or ~ 220 V, 6 A; *c*—terminal block with terminals and sockets, ~ 127, ~220 V, 12 V, 10—6 A *d*—single-socket wall bracket; *e*—telephone; *f*—alternating current rectifier, ~ 220 V; *g*—terminal block with terminals and sockets, ~ 220 V, 10 A; *h*—6—A switch; *i*—laboratory board with terminals and sockets, ~ 127, ~ 220 V, 200 V, 20 A; *j*—individual ventilation; *k*—basin; *l*—gas.

I. Work room:

1—writing table; *2*—drawing table; *3*—table for IZA-2 comparator; *4*—instrument cabinet; *5*—writing table; *6*—book case.

II. Photometer room:

1—MF-2 microphotometer; *2*—DSP-1 spectrum projector; *3*—work table; *4*—PS-18 spectrum projector; *5*—MF-2 microphotometer.

III. Photography room:

1—photographic work table; *2*—developing table with pan; *3*—cabinet for photographic plates and chemicals.

IV. Spectrograph room No. 1:

1—instrument cabinet; *2*—writing table; *3*—DG-2 generator; *4*— and *5*—tables for ISP-51 spectrograph; *6*—IG-3 generator; *7*—ISP-28 spectrograph; *8*—instrument cabinet.

V. Spectrograph room No. 2:

1—IG-3 generator; *2*—ISP-28 spectrograph; *3*—work table; *4*—table for spectroscope.

VI. Spectrometer room:

1—work table; *2*—IG-3 generator; *3*—ST.7 spectrometer.

VII. Sample preparation room:

1—fume cupboard; *2*—analysis balance; *3*—work table; *4*—cabinet for standards; *5*—cupboard for analysed samples; *6*—lathe; *7*—emery wheel; *8*—work bench; *9*—cupboard for analysed samples.

graph room (16 m^2), a spectrometer room (8 m^2), a photometer room (16 m^2), and a photography room (8 m^2). The total area of the small laboratory is 72 m^2.

A medium-size spectral analysis laboratory (Fig. 85) has in addition another spectrograph room (24 m^2) and a work room (24 m^2). Its total area is 120 m^2. A large spectral analysis laboratory has another photography room (8 m^2)

and the size of the photometer room is increased to 24 m². There are three spectrograph rooms with a total area of 72 m². The total area of the large laboratory is 160 m².

The sample preparation room should contain a work bench with a jaw vice and a drilling machine, a lathe, an emery wheel, an analysis balance, a fume cupboard with gas supply, and cupboards for storing the standards, reagents, dishes and samples.

The spectrographs are installed in the spectrograph rooms. Each spectrograph is fitted with generators. In addition, these rooms should have a supply of the gas required for using special excitation sources.

The spectrometer room is intended for visual quantitative analysis using a spectrometer. It should be dark, with close-fitting blinds at the windows.

TABLE 51. LIST OF FITTINGS OF SPECTRAL ANALYSIS LABORATORY

Fittings	Dimensions, cm			No. of articles			
	Length	Width	Height	Large lab.	Medium-size lab.	Small lab.	Control point
Table for KSA-1 spectrograph	250	80	90	1	—	—	—
Table for ISP-28 spectrograph	200	80	90	2	2	1	—
Table for ISP-51 spectrograph and its	180	60	90	1	1	—	—
lighting section	120	50	90	1	1	—	—
Table for microphotometer MF-2	100	80	80	2	2	1	—
Table for PS-18 (SPP-1) and DSP-1 spectrum projectors	100	80	80	2	2	1	—
Table for spectrometer and spectroscope	150	80	90	2	2	2	2
Work bench	150	70	80	1	1	1	1
Table for developing with pan	130	65	90	2	1	1	—
Table for photographic work	150	65	90	2	1	1	—
Work table	150	75	80	6	5	4	—
Drawing table	150	75	80	1	1	—	—
Writing table	150	75	80	5	3	1	—
Fume cupboard	200	60	250	1	1	—	—
Card cabinet for standards	80	40	180	1	1	1	—
Cabinet for analysis samples	120	50	200	2	2	1	—
Cabinet for photographic plates and chemicals	110	40	180	2	1	1	—
Cabinet for instruments	110	50	200	4	3	1	—
Book case	110	40	180	3	1	1	—
Clothes cupboard	110	40	200	—	—	1	—
Chairs				30	24	12	2

The photography room should also be dark, and light from the adjoining rooms should be prevented from entering it by means of a vestibule with a door and a close-fitting blind. In the photography room there should be a table for doing the photographic work, and a table for doing the developing, with a pan with a drain pipe, to which water is supplied via pipes. Two-thirds of the pan should be occupied by a wooden grille, on which stand the vessels containing the photographic solutions. A darkroom light with a cover of red glass should be mounted on the table or the wall.

The photometer room houses the spectrum projectors, the microphotometers, stands for viewing the spectrograms, a measuring microscope and a comparator.

The laboratory should be well supplied with cupboards, chairs, tables and other fittings. A list of the main fittings is given in Table 51. The tops of the tables for the instruments and the photographic work should be covered with lino. In instrument work rising stools are useful for adjusting the height of the seats.

As an indication of the power requirements for the standard spectral analysis laboratories, Table 52 gives data concerning the capacity of each piece of apparatus provided with current supply (including the lighting installations).

TABLE 52. CURRENT REQUIREMENTS

Name of installation or instrument	Requirement of one installation, kW	Requirement of each standard laboratory			
		Large lab.	Medium-size lab.	Small lab.	Control point
Grinding wheel	0·5	0·5	0·5	0·5	0·5
Drill	0·5	0·5	0·5	0·5	—
Lathe	1·5	1·5	1·5	1·5	—
Spark generator	0·7	3·5	2·1	1·4	—
Arc generator	3·0	6·0	6·0	3·0	3·0
Rectifier for feeding d.c. arc.	4·0	8·0	4.0	—	—
Stabilizer for microphotometer	0·1	0·2	0·2	0·1	—
Lamps for general lighting	0·15	2·1	1·5	0·9	0·3
Lamps for individual lighting	0·06	1·2	1·0	0·6	0·2
Total requirement of technical apparatus	—	20·2	14·8	7·0	3·5
Total requirement for lighting	—	3·3	2·5	1·5	0·5
Reserve for technical apparatus	—	2·5	2·7	1·5	1·0
Total requirement	—	26·0	20·0	10·0	5·0

Note. The grinding wheel, the drill and the lathe are supplied with three-phase current.

These data are useful in designing the electrical circuits of new laboratories. In this connexion the "coefficient of coincidence" should be taken into account. In the case of a spectral analysis laboratory it is about 0·6.

2. Plant and Materials

The amount of main and auxiliary plant, and also the materials that are required, depend on the type of laboratory. The total cost of plant and materials ranges from 75,000 to 250,000 roubles for a laboratory, and is about 25,000 roubles for a control point. If we take into account the yearly saving resulting from the advantages of spectral analysis methods, then, as experience shows, the entire cost of setting up a laboratory can be recovered in one to three years. Table 53 lists the main items of plant required.

The success of a spectral analysis laboratory depends largely on the correct selection of the auxiliary equipment (Table 54). Spectral analysis laboratories dealing with metals, alloys and other materials should possess standards for carrying out analyses. The standards kept at the laboratory will depend on the materials required to be analysed at the undertaking in question.

In the case of spectral analysis control points the auxiliary plant is limited to a vice, a grindstone and files.

In order to analyse ores, minerals and slags, the auxiliary plant will include, instead of metal and alloy standards and moulds, mortars, mixers and sets of screens for the production of powder samples.

Table 55 lists the main materials required in spectral analysis laboratories.

At control points the objects in this list that are required are rod-shaped electrodes 8 mm in diameter of Armco iron and electrolytic copper, and also disc-shaped electrodes 1–2 mm thick of copper sheet. Rods of aluminium and magnesium may be required, in order to make auxiliary electrodes.

3. Staffing Requirements

The staffing requirements of spectral analysis laboratories depend on the work carried out in the individual laboratories. The teams in large and medium-size laboratories consist of an analysis group employed on routine analysis, and a research group engaged in the development and application of new methods of analysis. Below we give typical staffing arrangements, for standard laboratories and control points.

In the case of the analysis groups at laboratories and control points, the figures given are for single-shift working. When two- or three-shift working is carried out, the figures should be multiplied by two or three, respectively.

TABLE 53. LIST OF BASIC PLANT

Plant	No. of articles: Large lab.	Medium size lab.	Small lab.	Control point	Rough price in roubles	Notes
1	2	3	4	5	6	7
SL-11 fixed spectroscope (or CL-13)	3	3	1	2	2500	
SLP-2 portable spectroscope (or SLP-3)	1	1	1	1	4000	
ST-7 spectrometer (in conjunction with IG-3 generator)	1	1	1	1	1500	Obtained when necessary in the case of small laboratories and control points
ISP-28 quartz spectrograph (in conjunction with IG-3 generator)	2	2	1	–	19000	
KSA-1 spectrograph with interchangeable quartz and glass optical system (in conjunction with DG-2 generator	1	1	–	–	40000	In the case of medium-size laboratories obtained when it is necessary to analyse very complex alloys, instead of one ISP-28
ISP-glass spectrograph	1	1	–	–	14000	Obtained when it is necessary to work in the visible region of the spectrum
UF-84 and UF-85 cameras and ISP-51 spectrograph	1	1	–	–	8000	
MF-2 microphotometer	2	2	1	–	6500	
PS-18 spectrum projector (or SSP-1)	1	1	1	–	2000	
DSP-1 double spectrum projector	1	1	–	–	5000	Obtained when necessary

Plant	No. of articles				Rough price in roubles	Notes
	Large lab.	Medium-size lab.	Small lab.	Control point		
1	2	3	4	5	6	7
IZA-2 horizontal comparator	1	1	–	–	3000	Obtained when necessary in the case of medium-size laboratories
MIR-12 microscope	1	1	1	–	1500	
STL table for viewing spectrograms	2	1	1	–	1000	
IG-3 spark generator	6	4	2	–	7500	Some of generators are listed with spectrographs and spectrometer
DG-2 arc generator	3	2	1	–	7500	Obtained when necessary
2VN-20 (20-A, 250-V) mercury rectifier	2	1	–	–	300	
RVS-1 time relay	4	3	1	–	500	Obtained according to number of spectrographs
Kler absorber	2	2	1	–	100	For laboratories analysing ores and minerals
Tables of spectral lines	2	2	1	–	20	
Atlases of spectra	copies		copy		5–30	For visible and ultraviolet region of spectrum

Staffing Arrangements at a Large Spectral Analysis Laboratory

1. Head of laboratory (engineering physicist, spectroscopist) 1
2. Deputy head (engineering physicist or chemist, spectroscopist) 1
3. Electrician-mechanic 1

(a) *Research group*

4. Senior engineer (physicist or chemist, spectroscopist) 1
5. Engineer (physicist or chemist) 1
6. Technician 1
7. Laboratory assistant 1

TABLE 54. LIST OF AUXILIARY PLANT

Plant	No. of articles			Notes
	Large lab.	Medium size lab.	Small lab.	
1	2	3	4	5
Standards for analysis of metals and alloys	–	–	–	Obtained when necessary. Standards for analysis of ferrous metals and alloys are produced in standard specimen laboratory of Urals Institute of Metals (Sverdlovsk, Vtuzgorodok, 9). Standards for aluminium alloys can be ordered from the All-Union Institute of Aviation Materials (Moscow urban council of national economy) and the All-Union Aluminium–Magnesium Institute (Leningrad).
Analysis balance with capacity of 200 g, weight difference up to 100 g	1	1	1	Obtained when necessary in the case of small laboratories.
Technical balance with capacity of up to 500 g with weight difference up to 1 kg	1	1	1	
Two-dial M–45 voltmeter for d.c. 3–15–75–150 V	1	1	1	
Current-voltage meter for a.c. and d.c. up to 6 A and 600 V	1	1	1	
High-voltage voltmeter up to 12,000 V	2	1	–	
Laboratory rheostat				
large, 23 Ω, 10 A	8	5	3	
30 Ω, 5 A	8	5	3	
60 Ω, 3 A	5	3	2	
400 Ω, 1 A	5	3	2	
LATR laboratory auto transformer	3	2	1	
Ferro resonance voltage stabilizer				
ENA–58, 750 W	2	1	1	
ENA–15, 100 W	2	2	1	

Plant	No. of articles: Large lab.	Medium size lab.	Small lab.	Notes
1	2	3	4	5
Table fan	3	3	2	
Electric stove	3	2	2	
Photographic light	4	2	2	
Vessels for photographic work				
size (cm) 24×30	2	2	–	
18×24	2	2	2	
13×18	3	3	2	
9×12	3	3	2	
Equipment for drying photographic plates and films	2	1	1	
Stopwatch	8	6	2	
Diamond or glass-cutter	3	2	2	
Thermometers:				
scale 0–50° with 0·5° divisions	3	3	3	
scale 0–150° with 1° divisions	2	2	–	
T–65 lathe (or S–1 table lathe) with set of tools	1	1	1	In the case of small laboratories obtained when necessary.
Two-sided emery wheel with 200–250 mm stone and an electric motor capacity 300–500 W	1	1	1	
Mechanical vice	1	1	1	
Parallel vice (jaw width 70 mm)	1	1	1	
Set of tools (hammer, files, bastard and smooth, power hacksaw with blades, electric soldering iron, flat pliers, round pliers, cutting pliers, monkey wrench, cutters, various screwdrivers, mechanical screwdrivers, slide gauge, micrometer, spirit level, number and letter marking irons)	1	1	1	
Moulds for casting electrodes	–	–	–	Depending on number of furnaces.
Agate mortar with pestle	2	2	1	For analysis of slags, minerals and ores.
Cast iron mortar with pestle	1	1	1	

Plant	No. of articles			Notes
	Large lab.	Medium size lab.	Small lab.	
1	2	3	4	5
Mechanical mortar	1	1	1	
Set of screens up to 300 mesh	1	1	1	
Mechanical mixer for powders	1	1	1	
Press (up to 5 tons/cm^2)	1	1	1	
Graphite crucibles 80 mm high, diameter 40 mm	20	20	—	
Porcelain crucibles (tall)	30	30	—	
Test tubes with lips: 100 cm^3	5	3	2	
250 cm^3	5	3	2	
Reagent bottles with ground glass stoppers, orange-coloured, capacity (litres): 0·5	5	5	5	
1·0	5	5	5	
2·0	3	3	3	
Material jars with ground glass stoppers, capacity (litres): 0·5	10	10	5	
1·0	10	10	5	
Brushes for washing flasks and test-tubes	10	10	3	
Goggles with plain and dark glasses	10	10	5	
Rubber gloves	5	5	5	
Two-meter rubber mats	6	5	3	
Slide rule	5	3	2	

(b) *Analysis group*

8. Group head (engineering physicist or chemist) 1
9. Technician 1
10. Laboratory assistant 2
11. Junior laboratory assistant 2

Staffing Arrangements at a Medium-size Spectral Analysis Laboratory

1. Head of laboratory (engineering physicist or chemist, spectroscopist) 1
2. Fitter-electrician 1

TABLE 55. LIST OF MATERIALS REQUIRED IN LABORATORIES

Materials	Unit of measurement	Rough yearly requirement of laboratories			Notes
		Large	Medium-size	Small	
1	2	3	4	5	6
"Spectrographic" photographic plates:	dozen				For rapid-test laboratory about 1000 dozen. Basic dimensions of plates 9×12 cm, some (about 20%) of plates should measure 9×24 cm.
Type I	dozen	400	350	250	
Type II	dozen	100	50	50	
Type III	dozen	100	50	50	
Panchromatic photographic plates	dozen	50	25	–	
Infrachrome 760 photographic plates	dozen	50	25	–	
Positive cinefilm, 16 GOST units	m	100	100	–	Obtained when necessary
Negative cinefilm, 65 GOST units	m	100	100	–	
Photographic paper No. 5, 18×24 cm	sheet	100	100	–	
Normal photographic paper No. 2, 18×24 cm	sheet	100	100	–	
Sulphite crystals	kg	20	20	20	
Soda crystals	kg	20	20	20	
Hyposulphite	kg	20	20	20	
Metol	kg	0·5	0·5	0·5	
Hydroquinone	kg	2·0	2·0	2·0	
Potassium bromide	kg	0·5	0·5	0·5	
Acetic acid	litres	2·0	2·0	2·0	
Alcohol (distilled)	litres	12	12	12	
Spectrally-pure graphite electrodes diameter 6 mm, length 24 cm		10000	5000	5000	The "Elektrougli" works (Moscow region, Kudinovo station) produces S–1 spectrally-pure electrodes (maximum purity not containing boron), S–2 (containing boron), S–3 (corresponding to carbons produced earlier), S–4 (0·001–0·01% of silicon and titanium), S–5(for technological purposes).

Materials	Unit of measurement	Rough yearly requirement of laboratories			Notes
		Large	Medium-size	Small	
1	2	3	4	5	6
Armco iron:					
diameter 6 mm	kg	5	5	5	
diameter 8 mm	kg	10	10	10	
Red copper rod:					
diameter 6 mm	kg	10	10	5	
diameter 8 mm	kg	10	10	5	
Red copper sheet, 1–2 mm	kg	10	10	5	
Type 00 primary aluminium, rod, diameter 8 mm	kg	3	2	2	
Pure magnesium rod, diameter 8 mm	kg	3	2	2	
Metallic nickel rod, diameter 6–8 mm	kg	3	2	1	
Metallic cobalt rod, diameter 6–8 mm	kg	3	2	1	
Metallic tungsten rod, diameter 5–6 mm	kg	2	1	1	
Rubber tubing, diameter 3–10 mm	m	50	20	—	
LPRGS wire	m	100	100	50	
Magneto wire	m	50	50	25	
Plastilin	kg	1	1	1	
Absorbent cotton	kg	4	3	2	
Asbestos sheet	sheet	5	5	5	
Stationery	kg	40	30	20	
Filter paper	kg	5	5	5	
Graph paper	roll	3	2	1	
Tracing paper	roll	2	1	1	
Whatman paper	sheet	50	30	30	
Wrapping paper	kg	50	50	20	
Record books for recording analyses	—	30	30	20	
Analysis record sheets	sheet		50,000		

(a) *Research group*

3. Senior engineer (physicist or chemist, spectroscopist)	1
4. Technician	1

(b) *Analysis group*

5. Group head (engineering physicist or chemist)	1
6. Laboratory assistant	2
7. Junior laboratory assistant	2

Staffing Arrangements at a Small Spectral Analysis Laboratory or a Rapid (Spot) Testing Laboratory

1. Head of laboratory (engineering physicist or chemist)	1
2. Group head (technician)	1
3. Laboratory assistant	1
4. Junior laboratory assistant	1

Staffing Arrangements of a Control Point

1. Senior controller spectroscopist	1
2. Controller spectroscopist	1

These recommended staffing arrangements are approximate. Individual staffing arrangements will depend on the amount of routine analysis and research work.

It is advisable for purposes of consultation on electrical and radio engineering matters to have an electrical engineer attached to the laboratory, who can quickly detect faults in the generators and other equipment and tell the fitter-electrician how to carry out the repairs. Since this is not a full-time job, the services of an engineer from the electrical department or laboratory can be obtained. Those in charge, and the engineers and technicians should receive special training or be experienced in spectral analysis work. To speed up the application of the methods of spectral analysis and for a better understanding of its principles, the laboratory assistants should have had a secondary school education.

The spectral analysis laboratory should work in close conjuction with the chemistry laboratory. In this way complete analyses can be carried out rapidly and simply. It is a great advantage from the production viewpoint if the analytical laboratory where the spectral and chemical analyses are carried out, is controlled by a single individual.

4. SAFETY PRECAUTIONS AND CARE OF INSTRUMENTS

Satisfactory working conditions should be provided for the staff, and all work should be carried out with proper observation of the safety precautions.

The main factors determining whether the working conditions are satisfactory are the size of the building and the provision of adequate ventilation. There should be spaces of not less than 1·5 m between all the instruments in the laboratory. In accordance with the requirements laid down by the Institute of Work Hygiene and Sickness of the Academy of Medical Sciences of the U.S.S.R., each spectral analysis instrument with an excitation source should be allotted 70–100 m of the building, corresponding to an area of 20–30 m. The ventilation system should provide three air changes per hour. Immediately above each excitation source there should be an individual suction device independent of the main ventilation system, in the form of a hood connected to an exhaust box by means of a pipe 120 mm in diameter. On working with toxic materials the source should be placed in a fume cupboard. The lathes for shaping the electrodes should be fitted with dust removers.

The casings of spark and arc generators, and also of all the instruments used in conjunction with them, should be earthed. The floor near the sources should be covered with high-voltage rubber tiles measuring 90×200 cm. The electrodes and the operating regimes should be changed only with the generators disconnected. The red-hot electrodes should be placed in a metal container.

Open sources of ultraviolet light should be screened with dark glass, or else the workers in the laboratory should be provided with protective goggles of dark or plain glass.

All work connected with the photometry of the spectra by visual (spectroscope, spectrometer) and photographic methods (photometric interpolation, microphotometry) should be done in alternation with other work (assembling the standards, photographing the spectra, making calculations, etc.), so that the total time spent by the workers on photometry of the spectra does not exceed 4 hr per shift.

When looked after carefully and treated properly, instruments for spectral analysis will last dozens of years. They should be protected against dust. Dust should also be removed regularly from the walls and ceiling of the building housing the instruments. Dust can be removed from the unimportant optical components by means of a squirrel-hair brush which is provided with the instruments. To protect them against dust when they are not in use, the instruments should be covered with close-fitting covers.

The quartz and glass lenses, prisms, mirrors, dials and also the diffraction gratings require particular care. These components should be protected against acid and alkali vapours.

The optical system should be cleaned in extreme cases only. The dust from the important optical components can be removed by a stream of clean dry air with the aid of a rubber puffer. Optical components should not be touched with the fingers, as this leaves grease spots which are very difficult to remove. They can be removed by carefully washing the components in very pure ethyl alcohol or petroleum ether. Impure grease removers may leave further spots. Components should not be rubber, as this may permanently damage the optical illumination system, the dials, the mirrors and the diffraction gratings.

The screens of the spectrum projectors should be kept clean. No pencil or ink marks should be made on them. The screens, and also the object glasses of spectrum projectors and measurement microscopes can be cleaned of dust and dirt by means of a piece of clean damp rag.

The slits of the spectral instruments and the micrometer screws require very careful attention. The slits are cleaned by means of tracing or tissue paper. Metallic or other hard objects should not be used. Micrometer screws should not be turned using excessive force. No screws on the instruments should be turned unless this is necessary.

The plate-holders and other mechanical parts of the instruments exposed to friction, should be cleaned periodically to remove dust, dirt and rust, and lubricated with high-grade machine oil.

On using the generators care should be taken to avoid overheating them. If lengthy work is entailed, the generator rheostats can be cooled by means of a fan.

5. NEW INSTRUMENTS FOR SPECTRAL ANALYSIS

The rapid developments now taking place in science and engineering make ever-increasing demands on the spectral analyst, the chief of which are greater accuracy and speed of analysis.

The visual methods of spectral analysis are very rapid, but their accuracy is not high. In addition, the results of the analysis depend on subjective factors (e.g. the spectral sensitivity of the eye of the observer).

The photographic methods take more time than the visual methods, because far more time is taken in treating the photographic materials than in exposing them. The results obtained with these methods are most accurate, because the photographic plate gives the mean spectral line intensity during exposure.

The photo-electric methods combine the advantages of the visual and photographic methods, being both rapid and accurate.

With photo-electric recording the spectral lines are separated by means of special slits. The light from the lines falls on to photo-electric cells. During exposure the photo-electric current charges the capacitors. The magnitude of the light flux from the spectral lines is directly proportional to the charge of the capacitors. After exposure has been completed, the charges (or voltages) of the capacitors corresponding to the spectral line intensities, are measured by means of a sensitive galvanometer calibrated in intensities or the logarithms thereof.

A set of standards is used to plot the calibration curve. In later work this curve need only be checked periodically.

Our industry has developed several models of photo-electric instruments, the simplest of which are the photo-electric spectrum analysers. There are 1-, 4- and 6-channel instruments FESA-1, FESA-4, FESA-6.[79, 80] The number of channels corresponds with the number of spectral lines being recorded simultaneously. To split up the light into a spectrum an SL-3 optical spectroscope or an ISP-51 spectrograph is used. The light sources are ordinary arc and spark generators. The determination error with this method is the same as that with the photographic methods (2–5 per cent), the time taken to do quantitative analyses is 5–6 min.

In order to improve the accuracy of photo-electric methods of spectral analysis, ways have been devised for increasing the accuracy of assembly of the electrodes. Special scanning lenses are used to ensure accurate projection of the light source on to the spectrograph slit when the light source strays over the surface of the electrodes. The spectra are excited by means of GEU-1 high-stability generators with electronic control.[81] The spectra are recorded by means of stable photo-electric cells, the sensitivity of which varies very little with time.

A high analysis accuracy can be obtained with the FES-1 photo-electric spectrometer.[82, 83] Here again the light source is a GEU-1 arc generator with electronic control. The image of the light source is projected on to the slit by means of a scanning glass lens.

This instrument contains one channel. The line of the element being evaluated is compared with the undispersed light of the source. The chemical elements are evaluated in succession. The analysis error is 1·5–2 per cent of the content being measured. The time taken to evaluated one element is 3–4 min.

In the instruments described above, the light is split up into a spectrum by means of spectral instruments with a prism optical system. More up-to-date instruments called quantometers are also built, in which a diffraction grating is used to split the light up into a spectrum.

The DFS-10 quantometer[83–85] has 36 channels of which 12 are in operation simultaneously. The instrument can be quickly switched over from analysis of one type of alloy to another. On being switched over, the instrument is given a fresh programme: the channels corresponding to the new elements being evaluated are then connected and those of the old elements being evaluated are disconnected.

The light source is a GEU-1 generator. The illumination is stabilized by means of a quartz scanning lens. With this instrument elements can be evaluated with a relative error of about 1 per cent. The time taken to analyse a specimen with respect to 10 elements is 3–5 min.

Our industry is also producing various spectrographs with diffraction gratings, which open up new fields for spectral analysis.

REFERENCES

I. General Manuals, Handbooks, Tables and Atlases

1. Mandel'shtam, S. L., *Introduction to spectral analysis (Vvedeniye v spektral'nyi analiz)*, GITTL, Moscow, Leningrad (1946).
2. Prokof'yev, V. K., *Photographic methods of quantitative spectral analysis of metals and alloys (Fotograficheskiye metody kolichestvennogo spektral'nogo analiza metallov i splavov)*, Part I, GITTL, Moscow, Leningrad (1951).
3. Prokof'yev, V. K., *Photographic methods of quantitative spectral analysis of metals and alloys*, Part II, GITTL, Moscow, Leningrad (1951).
4. Sventitskii, N. S., *The spectroscope and its use (Stiloskop i ego primeneniye)*, GITTL, Moscow, Leningrad (1948).
5. Rusanov, A. K., *Spectral analysis of ores and minerals (Spektral'nyi analiz rud i mineralov*, Gosgeolizdat, Moscow, Leningrad (1948).
6. Bel'kevich, Ya. P., *Manual of the spectral analysis of metals (Rukovodstvo po spektral-nomu analizu metallov)*, Sudpromgiz, Leningrad (1950).
7. Sukhenko, K. A., *Spectral analysis of steels and alloys (Spektral'nyi analiz stalei i splavov)*, Oborongiz, Moscow (1954).
8. Borovik-Romanova, T. F., *Spectral-analytical evaluation of alkali and alkali-earth elements (Spektral'no-analiticheskoye opredeleniye shchelochnykh i shchelochnozemel'nykh elementov)*, Moscow, (1956).
9. Lomonosova, L. S. and Fal'kova, O. B., *Spectral analysis (Spektral'nyi analiz)*, Metallurg-izdat, Moscow (1958).
10. Smirnov, V. F., Striganov, A. R. and Khrshanovskii, S. A., *Organization and equipment of typical spectral laboratories (Organizatsiya i oborudovaniye tipovykh spektral'nykh laboratorii)*, Moscow (1952).
11. *Spectral analysis. Annotated index of Soviet work on spectral analysis from* 1931 *to* 1950 *(Spektral'nyi analiz. Annotirovannyi ukazatel' sovetskikh rabot po spektral'nomu analizu s* 1931 *po* 1950 *g)* (edited by S. L. Mandel'shtam). Izd. Akad. Nauk SSSR. (1955).
12. Materials of All-Union Congresses on Spectroscopy (Materialy Vsesoyuznykh sove-shchannii po spektroscopii), *Szv. Akad. Nauk SSSR., ser. fiz.*, Nos. 5 and 6 (1953); No 2 (1954); Nos. 1 and 2 (1955); No. 9 (1959).
13. *Materials of the Tenth All-Union Congress on Spectroscopy (Materialy X Vsesoyuznogo soveshchaniya po spektroskopii)*, Vol. 2, L'vov (1958).
14. Zaidel', A. N., Prokof'yev, V. K. and Raiskii, S. M., *Spectral line tables (Tablitsy spektral'nykh linii)*, GITTL, Moscow, Leningrad (1952).
15. Kalinin, S. K., Yavnel', A. A. and Naimark, L. E., *Atlas of arc and spark spectra of iron (Atlas iskrovogo i dugovogo spektrov zheleza)*, Metallurgizdat, Moscow (1953).
16. Rusanov, A. K. and Il'yasova, N. V., *Atlas of flame, arc and spark spectra of the elements (Atlas plamennykh, dugovykh i iskrovykh spektrov elementov)*, Gosgeoltekhizdat, Moscow (1958).

17. Kalinin, S. K., Yavnel', A. A., Alekseyeva, A. I., Marzuvanov, V. L. and Naimark, L. E., *Atlas of spectral lines for the quartz spectrograph (Atlas spektral'nykh linii dlya kvartsevogo spektrografa)*, Gosgeoltekhizdat, Moscow, (1959).
18. Kalinin, S. K. and Marzuvanov, V. L., *Atlas of arc and spark spectra of iron (Atlas dugovogo i iskrovogo spektrov zheleza)*, Metallurgizdat, Moscow (1958).
19. Kalinin, S. K., Naimark, L. E., Marzuvanov, V. L. and Ismagulova, K. I., *Atlas of spectral lines for the glass spectrograph (Atlas spektral'nykh linii dlya steklyannogo spektrografa)*, Gosgeoltekhizdat, Moscow (1956).
20. Taure, L. F., *Atlas of spectral lines for analysis by means of a spectroscope (Atlas spektral'nykh linii dyla analiza s pomoshch'yu stiloskopa)*, Riga (1957).
21. Taure, L. F., *Atlas of spectral lines for analysis of light metals by means of a spectroscope (Atlas spektral'nykh linii dlya analiza tsvetnykh splavov pri pomoshchi stiloskopa)*, Riga (1959).

II. Papers, Booklets and Other Literature

22. Sventitskii, N. S., *Zav. lab.*, *7*, 1371 (1938).
23. Kler, M. M., Use of PS–39 generator for spectral analysis of powder samples. *Inf.-tekh. listok LDNTP*, No. 49, Leningrad (1956).
24. Abramson, I. S., *Zav. Lab.*, *16*, 464 (1950).
25. Raiskii, S. M., *Zh. tekh. Fiz.*, *9*, 1719 (1939); *10*, 431, 459, 530, 908 (1940).
26. Yankovskii, A. A., *IFZh*, *1*, No. 10 (1958).
27. Derevyagin, N. P., *Zav. Lab.*, *19*, 1200 (1953).
28. Prokof'yev, V. K. *Izv. Akad. Nauk SSSR, ser. fiz.*, *9*, 691 (1945).
29. Kudelya, Ye. S., *Spectral analysis of carbon, phosphorus and sulphur in metals and alloys*, Gostekhizdat U.S.S.R., Kiev (1958).
30. Ust'yantseva, M. P., Quantitative evaluation of copper in steels by means of the spectroscope. *Inf.-tekh. listok LDNTP*, No. 3, Leningrad (1956).
31. Kudelya, Ye. S., and Dem'yanchuk, A. S., Evaluation of phosphorus in steels and phosphor-tin bronzes by means the spectroscope, *Inf.-tekh. listok LDNTP*, No. 17 (1953).
32. Tikhomirova, N. K., *Zav. Lab.*, *13*, 221 (1947).
33. Sventitskii, N. S. and Fedorov, M. F., *Zav. Lab.*, *13*, 626 (1947).
34. Sventitskii, N. S. and Shlepkova, Z. I., Spectral analysis by means of the ST–7 spectrometer. *Inf. tekh. listok LDNTP*, No. 18, Leningrad (1957).
35. Burakov, V. S., Collection of papers read at the first scientific and technical conference on spectral analysis, Minsk (1956).
36. Ovechkin, G. V., Paltarak, Ye. N. and Grinevich, V. A., *IFZh*, *1*, No. 5 (1958).
37. *Sensitometric handbook. Properties of photographic materials on a transpar nt backing* (edited by Prof. Yu. N. Gorokhovskii and S.S. Gileva), GITTL, Moscow (1955).
38. Mikulin V. P., *Photographic materials handbook*, Gosizdat "Iskusstvo", Moscow (1958).
39. Fishman, I. S., *Zav. Lab.*, *10*, 628 (1941).
40. Sorokina, N. N., *Zav. Lab.*, *19*, 1052 (1953).
41. Sorokina, N. N., Reducing the number of standards in carrying out spectral analysis. *Inf.-tekh. listok LDNTP*, No. 6, Leningrad (1955).
42. Kibisov, G. I., Rezvova, M. I., *IFZh*, *2*, No. 6 (1959).; Kibisov, G. I., *IFZh.*, *2*, No. 3 (1959).

43. Vvedenskii, L. Ye., *Zav. Lab.*, *5*, 1349 (1936).
44. Buyanov, N. V., *Izv. Akad. Nauk SSSR, ser. fiz.*, *19*, 174 (1955).
45. Koritskii, V. G., *Izv. Akad. Nauk SSSR, ser. fiz.*, *18*, 276 (1954).
46. Dem'yanchuk, A. S. and Kudelya, Ye. S., *Materials of the Tenth All-Union Congress on Spectroscopy*, Vol. 2, p. 535, L'vov (1958).
47. Tokareva, A. M., Collection of reports read at the first scientific and technical conference on spectral analysis, Minsk (1956).
48. Fishman, I. S., *Izv. Akad. Nauk SSSR, ser. fiz.*, *9*, 753 (1945).
49. Komarovskii, A. G., Parallel-graph method and system of standards for the analysis of alloy steels. *Inf.-tekh. listok LDNTP*, No. 71, Leningrad (1952).
50. Buravlev, Yu. M., *Izv. Akad. Nauk SSSR, ser. fiz.*, *19*, 166 (1955).
51. Kibisov, G. I., *Izv. Akad. Nauk SSSR*, *14*, 623 (1950).
52. Dem'yanchuk, A. S. and Ryabushko, O. P., *IFZh*, *3*, No. 4 (1960).
53. Bel'kevich, Ya. P., *Experience in the spectral analysis of copper-base alloys*, Sudpromgiz, Leningrad (1955).
54. Chirkinyants, G. A., *Spectral analysis of copper, brass and bronzes*, Sudpromgiz, Leningrad (1959).
55. Vorontsov, Ye. I., *Zav. Lab.*, *19*, 1180 (1953).
56. Taganov, K. I., Collection of reports read at the first scientific and technical conference on spectral analysis, Minsk (1956).
57. Burakov, V. S. and Yankovskii, A. A., *Dokl. Akad. Nauk SSSR*, *2*, 156 (1958).
58. Kiselevskii, L. I., *IFZh*, *1*, No. 6 (1958).
59. Finkin, K. Z., *Izv. Akad. Nauk SSSR, ser. fiz.*, *19*, 120 (1955).
60. Rusanov, A. K. and Khitrov, V. G., *Materials of the Tenth All-Union Congress on Spectroscopy*, Vol. 2, p. 102, L'vov (1958).
61. Zil'bershtein, Kh. I., *Zav. Lab.*, *19*, 443 (1953).
62. Feldman, C., *Analyt. Chem.*, *21*, 1041 (1949).
63. Gul'ko, I. S., *Trans. Minsk Medicinal Intstitute* (1960).
64. Rudnevskii, N. K., Ivagin, L. I. and Ivagina, L. N., *Izv. Akad. Nauk SSSR, ser. fiz.*, *14*, 698 (1950).
65. Vinnichenko, E. M., Zaidel', A. N. and Kaliteyevskii, N. P., *Vestnik LGU*, No. 11, 119 Leningrad (1954).
66. Pavlyuchenko, M. M., Akulovich, V. M. and Filonov, B. O., *Materials of the Tenth All-Union Congress on Spectroscopy*, Vol. 2, p. 516 (1958); Collection of papers read at the first scientific and technical conference on spectral analysis, Minsk (1956).
67. Kler, M. M., Method for approximate quantitative spectral analysis. *Inf. tekh. listok LDNTP*, No. 72, Leningrad (1952).
68. Belousova, M. I., *Izv. Akad. Nauk SSSR, ser. fiz.*, *18*, 291 (1954).
69. Buyanov, N. V., *Zav. Lab. 14*, 565 (1948).
70. Buyanov, N. V., *Izv. Akad. Nauk SSSR, ser. fiz.*, *12*, 439 (1948).
71. Abramson, I. S. and Fal'kova, O. B., *Zh. tekh. Fiz.*, *19*, 611 (1949).
72. Nalimov, V. V. and Ionova, K. I., *Zav. Lab.*, *18*, 301 (1952).
73. Nalimov, V. V. and. Ionova, K. I., *Zav. Lab. 18*, 305 (1952).
74. Nikitina, O. I., *Izv. Akad. Nauk SSSR, ser. fiz.*, *18*, 295 (1954).
75. Nikitina, O. I., *Materials of the Tenth All-Union Congress on Spectroscopy*, Vol. 2, p. 455. L'vov (1958).
76. Buyanov, N. V., *Izv. Akad. Nauk SSSR, ser. fiz.*, *19*, 89 (1955).
77. Nikitina, O. I., *Izv. Akad. Nauk SSSR, ser. fiz.*, *23*, 1159 (1959).

78. Methods for the spectral analysis of fluxed sinter and blast-furnace slag (code of practice). Ukrainian Scientific Research Institute for Metals, Khar'kov (1958).
79. AVERBUKH, M. M., IVANTSOV, L. M. and KANDINOV, A. V., *Zav. Lab.*, *20*, 57 (1954).
80. AVERBUKH, M. M., ARTSISHEVSKAYA, N. V., BELYAYEV, N. V., BUTUZOV, A. V., DAVYDOV, A. S., KUTOVOI, S. V. and STREL'TSOV, I. G., *Zav. Lab.*, *20*, 62 (1954).
81. DEMIDOV, M. I., OGURTSOVA, N. N. and PODMOSHENSKII, I. V., *Izv. Akad Nauk SSSR, ser. fiz.*, *19*, 72 (1955).
82. ABRAMSON, I. S., *Zav. Lab.*, *20*, 168 (1954).
83. PROKOF'YEV, V. K., *Izv. Akad. Nauk SSSR, ser. fiz.*, *22*, 737 (1958).
84. PODMOSHENSKII, I. V. and KONDRASHOVA, L. D., *Izv. Akad. Nauk SSSR, ser. fiz.*, *19*, 36 (1955).
85. LOBACHEV, M. V., PODMOSHENSKAYA, S. V., TRILESNIK, I. I. and SHADRINA, A. B., *Zav. Lab.*, *25*, 1013 (1959).
86. SHAYEVICH, A. B., *Methods of estimating the accuracy of spectral analysis*, Metallurgizdat Sverdlovsk (1959).
87. KALMANOVICH, I. Z., *Zav. Lab.* *19*, 1196 (1953).
88. BORBAT, A. M., SOSKIN, M. S. and FINKEL'SHTEIN, S. G., *Zav. Lab.* *21*, 313 (1955).
89. BORZOV, V. P. and TAGANOV, K. I., Spectral method of determining the composition and the thickness of metallic coatings. *Inf.-tekh. listok LDNTP*, No. 16, Leningrad (1951).
90. BORBAT, A. M. and SOSKIN, M. S., *Zav. Lab.*, *18*, 1114 (1952).

INDEX